Golden Stories

Liz Syred
Editor

Ist Edition 2013

Published by:
For the Right Reasons
38-40 Grant Street,
Inverness IV3 8BN
Tel: 01463 718844
Email: fortherightreasons@rocketmail.com
www.fortherightreasons.net

© 2013 Merkinch Community Centre, Inverness IV3 8AD

A CIPD catalogue record for this book is available from the British Library

CONTENTS

Acknowledgements

Forward

Introduction

Part I

Part II

Summary - Comparing and Contrast life in the 1940s to life in 2013

Glossary

Money comparison 'then' and 'now'

Acknowledgements

Thank you to all who have helped bring this book into being. Thanks first to Elsie Normington for providing me with the opportunity to do this piece of work and encouraging me throughout the project. I also want to thank everyone who has been willing to share their stories, from those at the Muir of Ord Art Class, the Royal Highland Hotel Lunch Club, Singing for Pleasure and other contacts in the community whom I have met along the way.

Thank also goes to Ann McLellan, who read the initial draft and Isla Cuthbert who proof read the final version. I am grateful to them both for their support, patience and endurance!

Finally, I want to thank my husband Richard for scanning and sorting all the photos, for also proof reading, encouraging and supporting me throughout the many hours I spent working on the text and for being my best friend.

Liz Syred
Editor

Forward by Elsie Normington

Golden Stories was initiated as an extension of a new project called 'Golden Times' which was launched in Merkinch Community Centre August 2011. The Project provided a range of activities for people who are aged over 60 years and offered experiences in physical activity, lifelong learning and socialisation.

Since its inception, Golden Times has been very popular and over 200 people have regularly attended sessions and enjoyed meeting new people as well as learning new skills. The idea of Golden Stories emerged as an extension of the existing project. Many older people would share their memories when attending Centre groups and it was noted that these memories should be captured in some format.

Around this time, a class called 'Golden Gadgets' was already running very successfully where young people teach older people how to use mobile phones and other technology. The idea began to emerge that we could create an inter-generational project on oral history and seek to compare and contrast what life was like in 1940s and compare it with life in 2013.

Golden Stories therefore grew out of this background.

Concurrent with this, Liz Syred had begun to collate memories with members of an Art Group which was mainly attended by older people. This was a perfect synergy for the Golden Stories Project. The Project has therefore provided an opportunity for capturing a deep insight into the changes which have emerged over the past seventy years in our communities and lifestyle within the City of Inverness.

There is a range of memories shared from those who have lived in Inverness all of their lives and others who have moved from various parts of UK. Not only that, it has provided learning opportunities for young and old to learn media skills; share memories of their precious artefacts with each other; enjoy the experience of being filmed; having cameras enter their home and sharing their life stories. In the future, older people will also have an opportunity to join a drama group and perform a Production which includes some of these precious memories.

Grateful thanks is acknowledged to all those who have contributed their stories and given us the privilege of seeing a window into their lives. There are several other colleagues who contributed to the development of the project: Donald McLeod, Strategic Community Development Consultant and Robert Livingstone from Hi-Arts who met many times to help 'shape' the project. Also to Anne McDonald who facilitated our discussions on the project plan and funding bid.

Thanks to our Funders: Heritage Lottery Fund and Highland Council Discretionary Fund. Without these funds, this project would not have been possible.

Finally, I acknowledge most sincere thanks to Liz Syred, Editor who spent many hours, attending the Golden Stories sessions, interviewing so many people and collating all the material into this book - 'Golden Stories'.

Elsie Normington
Community Development Officer
Merkinch Community Centre

The Golden Stories project was initiated by Community Development Officer, Elsie Normington who had the idea of an oral history project which would compare and contrast by discussing, recalling and recording memories both past and present, bringing together different generations living in Inverness.

A couple of years ago I heard of a lady who had recently died who was considered to be the one person in her locality who knew everything there was to know about anything to do with the area. I asked if anyone had recorded the details. No-one had. It was sad to think that with her passing went so many valuable and interesting details of life in the Highlands in the 20th Century.

Not long after that, whilst sitting at the monthly Sunday Lunch Club held at the Royal Highland Hotel in Inverness, which I have the privilege to co-ordinate, I heard some interesting stories. Again, I thought that if these are not recorded they would be lost in the annals of time. This spurred me on to invite individuals to tell me their stories.

When I asked volunteers young and old if they would be willing to talk with me, many of them said "Oh, I don't think I have anything worth saying. I haven't had an exciting life." But memories, experiences and dramas in life are made up of small incidental things that we encounter every day. Often we do not realise what has changed until we look back and compare them against the present. Subtle changes come along which at the time appear insignificant. Each story in this book I believe has been worth recording and reading because it is personal, it is about people who I have met and spent time with and whom I believe are special and of value.

This book is a fascinating collection of individuals' recollection of life, brought together from a cross-section of randomly chosen people. Quotes about different topics from those who attended the Golden Stories workshop are also included. Some people have lived in Inverness and surrounding areas all their lives. Others were born in the Highlands and Islands, moved away and returned later in life. Still others have moved into the area from various places around the UK or further afield. My hope is that as you read this collection of stories you will catch at least a glimpse of their individual lives and something of their love for Inverness and its surrounding area.

There may be some historical inaccuracies, but in the context of this book, the aim has been to gather and record, compare and contrast the precious memories as they were spoken and remembered rather than be factually correct. Everyone was asked the same initial questions covering key topics ranging from schooling, courting, employment, shopping and the general way of life.

Golden Stories is divided into two sections. Part I consists of stories from people living in the 1930s and '40s, while Part II is much shorter with just a few stories of young people developing their lives today. You will appreciate there are many incidents I have not been able to record merely because of the constraints on time and space but I hope I have captured key memories.

It also draws together the discussions at the Golden Stories weekly workshops where the group discussed different topics each week. It draws on the memories and views of both old and young people and enables us to compare life past and present.

The combination of both younger and older people not only helps us see how life, values and society have changed, but also how some things in life continue across the generations. One lady said, "The world is not necessarily worse or better, it has just changed."

This has been a wonderful project which I have so enjoyed, and as the reader, as you are introduced to various people you will get to know them and leave them believing your life has been enriched from what you have learned about their lives.

1. Margaret Cowie

I was born in Glasgow in 1914. My first visit
to Phoineas near Inverness was when I was
six weeks old - a fortnight after the Great
War began. My mother travelled with me up on a steam train.
We left Glasgow at 11am and arrived in Inverness at five
o'clock that evening. We had to change trains at Inverness to
get to Beauly and when we arrived there was no transport of
any kind, not even a horse and cart. The horses and ponies had
been taken for war work. So my aunt came to meet us on her
bicycle. She carried our case which was a wicker-basket box
trunk, while my mother carried me four miles to Phoineas.
When we arrived my mother fainted!

My father was in the Police Force and as a result, during his
career we moved home from time-to-time depending on
which division he was in.

When I was a child we played with skipping ropes, singing
games, and at certain times of the year we girls would crochet
squares - the bigger the better - which we made into shawls
and blankets. At school boys and girls were always separated
so we had different playgrounds and didn't mix at all. Well
officially at least!

As a child I was very interested in Bible stories and I decided I
would like a Bible for Christmas. When it came, I got one but
then I looked round and saw what my sisters got. I wasn't
amused! However, my parents anticipated this and they had a
doll put aside for me. It was a china head doll. I also had a doll
with a leather body which I got from my father. By this time he
was stationed in the Gorbals which was notorious for its
poverty, deprivation and violence, with gangs fighting among

11

themselves. On one such occasion, a toy shop had been raided and my father was called to the scene. He had to go through the bins looking for clues and he found this doll made of pale grey kid's leather. He handed it in but it was never claimed and as was the practice, after a certain time span, he was allowed to keep the doll. So he brought it home and it became mine.

When I was young, as a family we came up to the Highlands for our holidays. I loved coming to Inverness. One year I went to Innellan near Dunoon, and although that was nice, I missed our regular trip to the Highlands. We couldn't do both because my father only got two weeks holiday a year. My granny was very religious and didn't approve of travelling on a Sunday. However, one particular time we travelled up on the Sabbath but there was no direct train to Inverness. So, we came via Forres and Nairn to Dalcross Station. Aunt Kate was at the station to meet us and she told the porter that people were coming off the train at Dalcross. He was expected to stop the train for her. So obediently, he raised the signal, the train stopped there even though it wasn't supposed to. We were way up from the platform and had to jump from the carriage onto the ground.

When staying with my granny I went with her to the local Free Church and had to walk from Phoineas to Kiltarlity. My granny was a widow and always wore black to church as was the custom for widows at that time. We would then walk from there to Balblair to a Gaelic service having nothing with us but a packet of tea biscuits to keep us going. When we got there we would sit through the service not understanding a word of it. I remember sitting pulling the elastic of my hat until I got a slap on the knee from Granny for moving. I was supposed to sit perfectly still!

I started at Polmadie Primary School in the south side of Glasgow walking each way every day. I remember at that time we practically lived in the country as Glasgow was largely undeveloped – open, not built up and as vast as it is now.

I recall when I was five, on my first day at school, that there was a celebration for Princess Mary. I think it may have been to celebrate her engagement, and all the children dressed up for it nevertheless. I remember my dress; it had been my sister's first. It was made of tussore pure silk. It was cream and had smocking at the front. We were expected to bring our own mug and I attached mine to a ribbon carrying it over my shoulder. We then had a picnic in the school playground with lemonade and buns and a 'piece' – there were no lessons that day!

In the Infants' class there were little tables and chairs with arms and we would have a tray of sand and a taper of wood and were expected to write the letters in the sand, after which we would shake it and start again. That is how we learned to write. Having mastered this we were allowed a slate with slate pencils, and finally we progressed onto using a nib. We were not allowed to use a fountain pen at school, but I had a pink one with a tassel on the end which had come from America. Biros weren't invented then.

I used to go home for lunch. There were no school meals or anything like that provided at school.

At the age of eleven I had just recovered from pneumonia and just before I went back to school we were visiting a friend of my mother's and that was the day the future Queen Elizabeth II was born. I remember my mother and her friend talking, saying it was terrible that the Prime Minister had to be in attendance to confirm the gender of the child in case someone tried to change it to male if the baby was female!

When preparing for senior school I had to sit what was called a 'qualifying exam'. The exam was held in the high school you wanted to move to, not the school you were attending, which was very daunting and you were only allowed to take a pen and ruler. Once there, I had to wear a uniform. It consisted of a navy blue gym tunic. My P.E. teacher didn't approve of collars and so we had to wear white square neck blouses. I left Strathbungo School at the age of thirteen when as a family we moved house. I had to transfer to North Kelvinside School. It was quite different. There were two schools on the one site; an old one and a new one. There was also a big house which was divided into two – one being of oak and one being of mahogany. Every girl pupil would get one day a week there learning various skills such as: sewing, how to set a dining room table, make a lunch, how to sit properly at the table and how to serve the lunch so we would know how to behave.

On leaving school I went to work in the Counting House in Trerons in Sauchiehall Street. It is not there anymore as it burnt down many years ago. It was a lovely, beautiful place. They had French Polishers who worked from one year to the next, polishing all the mahogany counters. The staircase was also mahogany and carpeted. The ground floor was not carpeted but covered in cork linoleum. They had a floor walker who wore tails. I worked in the cash desk and counting house. I had to have everything right. My wages were 7/- a week and if my books were right at the end of the week I got an extra 2/- I worked from 9am to 6pm Monday to Friday and half day on Saturday. However the staff in Argyle Street worked the same hours during the week but to 9pm on a Saturday. The shop was eventually taken over by Lewis'.

There was the Ladies Mantle Department, which would now be known as the Dress Department, and a Millinery Department which also had a millinery workshop attached. The buyers would go over to Paris for Fashion Week and return with one or two unique hats. Those working in the workroom would make copies of the hats to sell in the shop. Hats would cost somewhere in the region of five guineas - which was a lot of money for a hat - but we had a lot of West End customers who would pay that kind of money. They would also request a hat to match their outfit and so the millineries would make them accordingly.

I remember going to the Empire Exhibition in Glasgow in 1936 or '37. The exhibition was at Bellahouston Park and they had buildings constructed for this exhibition. I was there once with the girls from work. There was artists' work and garden work. They had the old 'Black Houses' with a fire in the middle and a hole in the roof. Women sat outside with spinning wheels, spinning out the wool so they could knit. The exhibition must have been open for about six months.

Just before World War II, my sister Betty and my brother Ian were to be evacuated up North. My mother wouldn't be parted from them. Our two grannies lived up in the Highlands and so my father retired from the Police and took over the village shop in Kirkhill. I worked as the shop keeper. It was quite a lot of work between running the shop, managing the rationing and all that. People would bring in their coupons to buy their groceries and then, each week, we would log the coupons and send them off to the Food Office.

In the house we used both coal and bottle gas. We had gas irons and flat irons. The irons were hollow and there was a hole at the end of it. An iron shaped mould would be put into the fire to heat up and then shove it in the iron.

We had two tubs and a boiler for the washing. We had a wash house and I would go out early in the morning and light the boiler to get the water hot. There was a wringer and a big mangle. In Glasgow paper shops used to have a mangle and you could take your damp washing i.e. sheets, table cloths etc. and they would put them through the mangle and fold them ready for ironing for you for 6^d.

My mother would always set the table with white linen tablecloths. The slop bowl would sit at one end and I remember one day she was having visitors for afternoon tea and my brother came in and said, "Who is drinking tea out of the bowl?" He didn't realise it was the slop bowl.

As a family we always ate together. When we were young we would eat porridge made with oatmeal. While babies were being weaned the oatmeal would be steeped at night and then the top off the oatmeal would be skimmed off and that was made into porridge for them.

We used to get eggs sent to us in Glasgow from my granny. She would wrap the eggs in paper, pack them into a robust cardboard box which had twelve sections and send them to us. Mother would post the box back to her putting sweets in each section. Rabbits, chicken or pheasants would be transported as they were, just with a label on.

We owned both the shop and the field adjoining it and my father would plough it and grow all sorts of vegetables. We also had bees which gave us honey and owned our own hens.

During the war, Achnagairn House, which is situated in Kirkhill, was a convalescent hospital for soldiers from Eastern Europe including Poles, Canadians and Czechoslovakians. Within the Army the Canadian Eskimos were experts at hooking salmon and they would go down to the foot of the Upper Falls at Kilmorack near Beauly and hook the salmon as they leapt up stream. That was how they got fresh fish to eat at the camp. It was fascinating and we used to go and watch them.

I knew my husband Alex from when we were young. His family came from Motherwell and his mother and my mother were friends. His family would come up to the Highlands to visit relatives and we would all meet up, and as children we played together. I never thought I would ever marry him but there you are. When we were courting we would go into Inverness and go to the pictures. We didn't have a car, which meant leaving the film early to catch the last bus. There was also an Air Force band based in Lentran House and they had a lovely orchestra. There used to be dances in the main hall which we were able to attend. The rest of the building was divided into billets.

We married in 1942. My wedding was a very quiet affair. We got married in the vestry of Wardlaw Church because all the customers at the shop threatened to come to the church and I was very shy and didn't want that. When I got married the clothes were all on coupons. You wouldn't have borrowed a wedding dress or hired one like people do now. I wore a powder blue dress with a basque over it with brown water lilies, brown hat, brown suede shoes and bag with a bouquet of spring flowers. Our reception was held at home. We saved up coupons for a roast, we had our own chickens and we had two ladies who did the catering. We hired china and cutlery from Burnett's in Inverness. The bridal table had a special tea set with a white lace pattern. It was a lovely wedding. We had a Canadian band which came from Achnagairn House

I remember my sister was married first and I was her bridesmaid. No-one took snapshots then. Official wedding photographs were taken at a photography studio in Inverness. Sadly by the time we found out that our photo never came out properly the best man had gone back to the Army. So my sister and her new husband had to get dressed up again, buy another bouquet and go and get another photo taken. When I got married I said I didn't want any fuss at all.

Our honeymoon was in Glasgow and lasted just over two weeks. I remember we stayed in a hotel in Charing Cross. There were barrage balloons in the sky, no lights in the tram cars or streets.

I also recall years later when the Queen came to Beauly to open the House of Beauly. Prior to this my husband had had a stroke and one of the Councillors involved in the arrangement of the event said that a number of tickets were to be allocated to people who were disabled, and we were offered two. Just before we left the house a neighbour gave my husband a red rose button-hole to wear in his jacket. When the Queen came along she stopped and spoke to him asking if he knew the name of the rose. Sadly, due to his stroke he couldn't speak. However, someone in the crowd took a photo of the Queen speaking to him and gave it to us. A lovely memory.

A major change I have noticed is the amount of houses that are in Inverness now. Every village is four times the size it was and people's way of life is so different. I just love the Highlands. When I was young I only ever wanted to come here and that has never changed.

2. Annie - An old Invernesian

I was born in 1923 in Cullicudden on the Black Isle between Culbokie and Cromarty. Mine was a home birth in a little cottage on the farm that my father owned. I have one brother and one sister.

I went to the local primary school at the age of five. I would walk one mile every day unless it was stormy – I hated thunder storms - then my father would take me and collect me on his motor bike which had a side car. When it was snowing my father would take us on a snow plough. I remember it so well. One Christmas my father drove us and other local families to school on the plough.

In the summer we would come home for lunch. We always had more time then so it was not difficult to come home. However in the winter we would stay in school and have lunch there. We would take a sandwich and a flask of tea or cocoa which the teacher would heat on the big stove in the classroom.

I loved playing 'houses' and with my dolls. I used to have trees at the end of the garden and I would have little bits and pieces making up my house and my dolls sitting on little stools. When I played with my brother and sister and we would play a lot of skipping, hopscotch and such like.

My father had relatives down in Dunfermline and so when we were children we often went there for a week every summer - a wee break together for us all.

As a family we ate together apart from breakfast. This was because as a farmer, my father would be up and out on the farm very early in the morning. We would have had porridge for breakfast and I remember so well the soup my mother made - it was broth, beautiful broth. It tasted so good the first day but by the second day it had seen better days! My father would shoot rabbits and we would have rabbit stew. We also ate a lot of herring and at weekends we had meat from the shop - not the farm! For puddings we used to have semolina - maybe with stewed fruit - creamola or sago which I hated. Anything that was easy to make because time was short.

Though I was very young at the time, I recall my father got a wee car and on occasions he would take us into Inverness. There was no bridge then so we would go round through Beauly. My father had sheep and every June he would shear the sheep. Then, he and my mother would take it up to Pringles in Inverness and swap the wool for knitting wool and tweed. Mother could make all our winter clothes with the tweed and she had a friend who knitted jumpers for us with the wool she got.

At the age of eleven I transferred to Dingwall Academy. I travelled on the school bus. I went to the very old school. Then, when I was in the fourth year, I moved up to the newly built Academy which has now also been demolished and another new school has been built on the same site. We didn't come home at lunch time from Dingwall because it was far too far but we would take a sandwich and make some tea using the kettle and tea diffuser which was there for our use.

I didn't like French, but I did like Maths, English and Latin - which we did in the first year. I am not sure what after-school clubs there were because we had to catch the school bus home as soon as school finished.

I left school at seventeen. In those days someone in the family was expected to stay at home and help. My sister went to Craibstone; a private girls' school, where they taught sewing, cooking and the like. She was very good with her hands and it was expected she would be at home. However my sister decided to get married to a farmer who lived quite near and, although I had sent off my application for nursing, I couldn't go having instead to stay at home and help. I didn't want to be at home, but at the time my mother wasn't very well and I couldn't just leave her. So I left school and worked for my mother until I got married in 1947 at the age of twenty three.

I met my husband at the local farmers' dance in the hall in Culbokie. They were members of the Young Farmers Club. We used to go dancing on Friday nights. I just love dancing. The old hut where we often went to meet was near my home. The music would consist of two accordions and a fiddle - I assure you that would be quite loud enough and the floor would be bouncing up and down, up and down - it was just such good fun. We would take our bicycles and we would leave them on the side of the road knowing they would still be there when we came out.

When we started going together, my husband had a car but the war was on and you weren't allowed to take your car anywhere because of fuel rationing and in case the car lights showed up in the night. If you did use the car and got caught you would be in trouble, so he used to take his bicycle. Anyway, after some time a few of the young farmers would use their car, putting something in the boot which if they got stopped they would say they were taking to the local Smithy for repair! That was just the way it was.

In those days, when going out, I had a choice of two dresses and it was a case of this one will do this week and then the other one the following week because we couldn't afford lots of clothes.

My husband bought his farm in 1943. We got engaged in 1944 marrying in 1947 in the Free Church in Bank Street, Inverness. My wedding dress was plain white which had a carnation design in the material. It was called Princess style. I think it was bought with coupons and I had a bouquet which was made up with carnations to match the dress. We spent the first night in Nairn and then took the train to Edinburgh for one week's honeymoon – you didn't go far in those days. We stayed at the Barnton Hotel. We then went up to Aberdeen and stayed with some friends for a few days before returning to our new home. There was no house on the farm when he bought it, but he built it in preparation of us getting married. It is still there today with various alterations and additions. When we moved in it was very basic. There was no furniture or electricity until 1953. We used mainly Tilly lamps but had other lamps with shades that had to be cleaned every day. We had a beautiful sideboard which my husband had got from someone a long time previously. We had a table in the kitchen and a bed. We had very little until we had saved up and could buy it. For example, there was no such thing as an electric kettle. For wedding presents we got silver trays, plates and two cases of silver cutlery. We even got two tea sets. We just gathered things as we went along. We didn't have credit cards. A little while later and before the family was born, like my mother had done before me, I started breeding hens. I had quite a few hen houses around the farm. I fed them twice a day and I would take the eggs I gathered and sell them to a man in Dingwall which paid for our 'messages' every week. We had to do that because we weren't well off at the time.

I did my shopping in Dingwall once a week. I would go to Winlows the Grocer and giving him my line he would go through it gathering together my items, wrap them in brown paper, tying the parcel with string - not even a paper bag - and that was that!

Our first holiday after I was married was when my son Grigor was aged two and I was expecting my daughter Katherine. We decided to have a wee break and we went down to the Trossachs. It was only after the family had grown up that we could afford a lot of lovely holidays.

I think the biggest changes that have happened here have been the two bridges – Kessock Bridge linking the Black Isle with Inverness and Cromarty Bridge leading up to Invergordon and that area. That has opened up the surrounding area and made everything more easily accessible.

For me personally a major event has been having my family. I love living here, I love my garden and the hills – this is my home.

3. Willie Geddes

I was born in Inverness in 1926. I attended Central Primary School and then went on to the High School. At that time you didn't get a choice of what subjects you went into. Therefore when it was my turn, they were short of people for the French and Latin classes so I got shoved into that. But I wasn't interested in those subjects. The Latin teacher was shell-shocked from World War I and he was very strange so I didn't enjoy school.

As a lad I attended Boys Brigade. There were ten different companies in Inverness and I was a drummer in the 5th Company band in East Church which was the biggest company in Inverness at that time with over sixty boys. We used to attend various classes during the week and I was in the rambling classes, ambulance training and the like.

A major event for me was the historical pageant which was performed from Wed 2nd to Sat 5th August in 1939. It was a fundraiser for the Isobel Fraser Home of Rest and it was held at the Northern Meeting Park. It was organised by Vice-countess Gough of Inshes House. She wrote the script, directed two scenes and jointly, with Mrs A D McPherson, wife of General McPherson of Holm House, organised the whole production. It was a market scene with a replica of the Town Hall with all the officials and Town Crier who went around collecting the pennies. I remember him making his announcements in the 'old' Invernesian language. I played the part of a young vandal in the town square. I had to annoy the local Bobbies by hitting them with stones and then running away. The pageant lasted four days and every day I walked up from King Street to the

Northern Meeting Park dressed in a brown dress, my face, body and legs all covered in brown sun tan. I had a great time.

I enjoyed cycling and on occasions I even cycled to Invergordon, a journey of twenty-four miles to see our grandparents. My brother and I, along with friends, would play catty. We also played marbles, and hide-and-seek. Where we lived in King Street there were lots of empty buildings and we would clamber in and out of them. We would go swimming in the river - in fact we spent a lot of time in the water. We would go down to the Greig Street Bridge, wait for the tide to come in and dive off it into the river. I also enjoyed fishing in the canal. There seems to be so many seagulls now and I think that is because no-one goes up the Loch Ashie Moor anymore and pinches the seagull eggs. There is only a couple of months in the year when you can take them, and we would nip down there collect them and then sell them to Willie Ferguson in the Highland Fish Shop in Union Street. He would give us something from the shop – half a pound of mince for example and then he would sell them in his shop.

Holidays were not such a major event in those days. When you went on holiday you generally went to your auntie's or some relative and so, as lads, we enjoyed going camping at the grounds of Holm House every weekend with the Boys Brigade.

I left school at fourteen and started off as a message boy for the butchers in Drummond Street. I got 2/6^d. It was an old established butcher firm and I stayed there for about two years of my five year apprenticeship, before being called up for National Service in March 1944.

At that time Ernest Bevin, Minister of Labour and National Service in the wartime Coalition Government, started his campaign placing every tenth person called-up down the mines. They were known as the 'Bevin Boys'. Several of my pals volunteered for the regular services in case they landed down the mines. They would say to me, "Willie don't get put down the mines there is plenty coal in the cellar!" No-one wanted to go down the mines because many Conscientious Objectors were sent down the mines as an alternative to military service. So the 'Bevin Boys' were also seen as 'Conchies'. I just took a chance and finished up in the Navy. None of our family had ever been in the Navy so I was the first. I ended up at Butlins holiday camp in Skegness and I was in active service for a few years until I was demobbed in 1946. I was sent to a hospital between Bath and Bristol where I trained for six months to be a nurse. I was then sent to work on HMS Jerusalem hospital ship, an old Italian liner which had been refurbished. It was an odd crew: there were two captains; Captain Black and Captain White and the different crews were made up of guys from all nationalities. In fact it was just like the League of Nations!

We left Liverpool on the troop ship across the Panama Canal and finished up in Sydney. From there we had to cross the desert and when we arrived at the other side there was a bloke walking up and down the railway platform playing the bagpipes – no idea how he got there! From there we picked up the hospital ship and went to the Admiralty Islands where we acted as base hospital for any activity in that area. During that time bombs were dropped in Hiroshima and Nagasaki so we moved up to Hong Kong to act as base hospital there for three months. Then we took the Japs, many in strait jackets, back to an island off Japan where they were cared for.

When I returned to England I was sent to a hospital in Southport where I got demobbed. I could have found a job down there but I wanted to get home. But I couldn't get a job in Inverness. I went to see the Matron at the Royal Northern Infirmary Community Hospital (RNI) but she stated there was "no such thing as a male nurse. Try Craig Dunain", which was the Inverness District Asylum, but I said I wasn't trained to be a mental nurse. Sadly she wouldn't hear of it so I went back to the butchers. It was a lot of heavy work lifting 300lbs sides of meat up and down the stairs.

We got two weeks holiday a year, plus Christmas Day and two days at New Year. I remember we had two days off at New Year because the manager of the butchers would take his racing bike apart the first day, clean it up and then put it all back together again on the second day.

I remember the worst time was when bread was rationed. That was tough. Bread rationing was introduced just after the war and lasted up until 1948/49. It cost 4/6^d for a loaf and a further 6^d if it was wrapped. Meat cost 10^d a week and 2^d for corned beef.

I married Barbara Sutherland in January 1953 in St Mark's Church, Huntly Street and had our reception in MacDougall Hotel in Church Street, now the Clansman. We then travelled down to Glasgow on the train for our honeymoon and stayed there for a week.

Our first home was in Eastgate - above the butchers. It consisted of two rooms and a little kitchen, it had a gas fire, electricity and coal fire and there were fifty-two steps from the street up to the door and no outside space. Getting furniture in and out of there was a nightmare. We lived there for nine years and then moved to Hilton. It was a council house in a good position and in 1963 we bought it, I gutted it and refurbished it and I am happy to say that is where I stay now.

27

4. Betty MacRae

I was born at home in Glasgow in 1928. It would have been a midwife who delivered me in those days I suppose. I was one of six and I was the second youngest.

I started school at the age of five. I walked to school and I remember howling the first day because I had been left! I remember the teacher giving me plasticine to play with to keep me quiet.

I am not boasting, but they used to have a Dux Medal on a blue ribbon which was given out every month and I used to get it quite a bit.

Each year, every holiday we used to come up to the Highlands on the train, staying with the two grannies and an aunt who was a Postmistress. We spent our time between the three of them. My mother would pack a hamper and all our clothes and we would come on the train to Inverness and then get a taxi up to Kiltarlity. I loved the taxi seats where they were folded against the cab and you had to flip them down to sit on them. I thought this was great.

We moved to Inverness two days after war started. My father sent my mother, my younger brother and I up to Kiltarlity to stay with my granny. We stayed there for two months and during that time I went to Culburnie School. I thought it was very funny because they used slates and slate pencils and everyone was in the same room. When I was in Glasgow we had used pens and jotters and the classes were divided according to age. I attended there for about two months but then our family moved to Kirkhill and so I had to go to

28

Inchmore School. I walked down there and home again which was approximately a mile each way.

As a child, I went to the Brownies, and then moved up to the Guides and onto the Girls' Training Core. This was pre-training, preparing the young ones for going into the forces during the war. I started off as a Cadet and ended up as the Company Commandant. We used to do physical training, citizenship, crafts and drill. I did this for twenty years. I used to take the girls hostelling to Edinburgh, Arisaig, and Glasgow – all sorts of places for weekends sometimes for a week. Then in 1950 I took some of the girls from the Training Corps to Switzerland, then to Guernsey and on a cruise to Norway on an old refurbished war ship – it was great fun. We would also attend the Inverness Tattoo every year. It was held in the Northern Meeting Park and we would have to do something such as a dance or do the hula-hoop to music.

While in the Girls Training Corps, I was chosen to represent the county of Inverness-shire, to be presented to Princess Alexandra at a rally in Glasgow Cathedral. It was a lovely day. There were hundreds of people there. We had to march through the streets of Glasgow into the Cathedral.

We had a Border Leicester pet sheep called Trudy. We used to wonder how she managed to get into the kitchen. Then one day I watched and she lifted the latch of the gate with her nose, then with her leg she pulled the gate open and off into the kitchen she would go. We also had a hen that sat on Trudy's back and the sheep would wander round the field with the hen on her back.

At twelve I sat an exam to get into the old Inverness Royal Academy up in the Crown area. High school was very different and I didn't like it. It was so big in comparison to primary school. There was one teacher – a French teacher and she was horrible and she put me off French for life.

My uniform consisted of a navy blue gymslip, royal blue blazer, black stockings, white blouse, royal blue and gold tie. It was compulsory to wear it.

I travelled by public bus into town. At lunch time my friend and I used to walk down Stephen's Brae to Burnett's the bakers and get a pie or something like that and then walk back again.

Only academic subjects were taught, so we didn't get sewing or anything like that. I left school at the age of sixteen and I took over working in the village shop which my father owned. All during the war the shop was attached to the side of the house, later it moved to a building across the road and then finally it became the village Post Office.

My father, having been a policeman was in the Home Guard and was the Quarter Master Sergeant. He used to drill the men. Our sitting room was full of guns – machine guns - as well as goggles as they didn't have anywhere else to keep them. It was just so like Dad's Army. I remember one night the lieutenant, who was just like Captain Mainwaring but was a postman, came to the door at one o'clock in the morning and shouted and knocked on the door, "Duncan, get up out of your bed the Germans have landed." It was a false alarm but they really did think they had landed. They did their drill round Kirkhill with poles and twigs in their helmets. It was hilarious.

We actually didn't go to Inverness very much because we didn't have cars and there was just the bus. You wouldn't pop in and out like we do now.

My friend and I would go into Inverness on Saturdays to the cinema and we would go to the Carlton Tea Room in Inglis Street for high-tea. It was beautiful, and then after the film we would go to the Caley for a coffee afterwards. When we went to the cinema there would be a supporting film and then the main film would come on.

I remember occasions when the shop would close and there would be a knock at the door and a customer wanted something. The soldiers based at Achnagairn House would come for cigarettes. My father would get quite annoyed with that, but that is what people did then. After all it was a grocer's shop! In the shop we had a trunk that stored oatmeal and I would have to weigh it out for the customers. Nothing was pre-packed then. Biscuits were loose and people were only given so many. Rationing was in place so we had to be careful to make sure people only got what they were entitled to. I worked in the shop for about eight years. I then went to a castle near Glasgow to work for a family. They wanted a companion - someone young to look after the two children as the lady was an older mother in her fifties. We stayed there for part of the year and then we went to London to Prince's Gate for the other part of the year, and that is how I got to the Coronation. The cousin of the lady of the house had been Chaplin for the Queen so she got tickets. We had a seat in the Mall. We had to get up at four in the morning and I remember it rained all day. The golden coach was beautiful and I specifically remember the Queen of Tonga as she sat in an open coach in the rain, no umbrella, smiling at everybody. I really enjoyed that. I worked for that family for about two years but I had to come home and look after my mother because she had had a heart attack. I looked after her for ten years.

By this time I was living at Portree-Allan and I had a car and I drove to work every day. I was also free to travel which I enjoyed a great deal. I travelled all over the place including Canada, America, and the Continent, to name a few.

Then I went for an interview for a receptionist post at the new Raigmore Hospital, which opened in 1970. Prior to that the hospital was used by the Army and the wards were all different single storey buildings with two rows of beds in each building. I had never done anything like it in my life but I got the job. No sooner had I got the job, I resigned! I hated it. However, within a week of leaving they contacted me and persuaded me to stay on and I stayed there for the next eighteen years.

I retired twenty-five years ago. I don't know where the time has gone. For several years I did voluntary work as receptionist at the Highland Hospice which I found very rewarding. I have remained living in Kirkhill and I am very happy here. I continued to travel returning to America and Canada and thoroughly enjoyed myself. Over the past twelve years I have attended the Muir of Ord art class which meets every Saturday morning. It is a super class where I have met some lovely people and had a lot of fun. I work with pastels and have the opportunity of exhibiting my work along with the rest of the group in our bi-annual exhibitions.

I am not a city girl and I love the peace and quiet of living here in the Highlands. The scenery inspires me which in turn influences my paintings. It is home.

5. Alec & Jean Murray

Alec: I was born in 1928 on a farm in Forfar. As a family we moved around quite a lot. I started school at the age of five and attended St Cyris School near Montrose. For most of my time in primary school I didn't go home at lunch time but we didn't have school dinners either. My twin brother and I just took a piece. I remember at one school we got a plate of soup for halfpenny. If there were several children in one family then the price of the soup was cheaper but that was it.

I used to play football and rounders and 'china' with the girls as well! Attending country schools meant that we always got lessons on gardening and how to grow crops.

I moved to secondary school when I was twelve to Bell Baxter School in Coupar. When I left school I got jobs on various farms and then when I was seventeen I joined the army. After I joined the army my twin brother decided he was going to join up too, so we went off and did our army training and then went to Singapore in 1948. Three months into our time in Singapore the communist war broke out and we were shipped off to Malaya and then to Korea for nine months and then were sent home.

On our return we landed up at Fort George where I stayed for two and a half years. During that time I would go dancing in Ardersier and that is where I met Jean.

Jean: I was born at home in a flat above the only chemist in Grant Street in 1933.

I went to Merkinch Primary School and then on to the High School at the age of twelve.

My key memory of Merkinch School was the lovely Headmaster Mr McCrane. He would stand with his watch in his hand waiting for us all coming into school in the morning and he would say to me "I don't know why you are late this morning; you only live a few steps away from the school. The reason I was late was because I had to do a bit of shopping for my granny in the grocers across the road. When I was ten my granny died and we moved away to Elgin for a couple of years but then we returned to Inverness and back to Grant Street.

I left school at fifteen and started work at Pringles Holm Mills. I worked from eight in the morning and finished at five at night with an hour for lunch. I got paid £1.50 a week and out of that I had to pay a shilling to the Union and one shilling for bus fare. I stayed there two years but then heard about a job in the Balmoral Restaurant in Queensgate. A couple of years later I went to work at the Station Laundry which was the best paid job of the lot. I got £12/3- a week which was a big difference to what I got in the other jobs! The Station Laundry was located beside the station where the car park is now and my job was to clean the sheets and tablecloths from the hotels in and round Inverness and those in Perth and about and clean the headrest and armchair covers from the first class carriages on the trains. It was a good job.

We married in 1953 which meant I had to give up my job. We lived with my mother who I looked after and then I had my children and stayed home to bring them up. I had triplets first: Mathew Mark and Amanda, but sadly they only survived three days. There was nothing wrong with them but they were premature and in those days there wasn't the science and medical equipment to keep them alive. The doctor said it was an amazing that Alec being a twin had triplets! We then had five more children all of whom are grown up and have families of their own. We have twelve grandchildren and at least twelve great grandchildren which is lovely.

Alec: We met at a dance in Ardersier and I met her and that was it. She gave me a lot of cheek but I chased her. She ran into the toilet and nearly caught my hand in the door and I said to her "You wait till you come out. I will get you." My twin wanted to go with her too.

Jean: Not knowing him very well, he said to me "I will meet you in town and we will go to the pictures." So I went and was standing watching him and his brother from across the road. They were dressed the same.

Alec: I called over to her and said, "Are you going to stand over there all day?"

Jean: I ran over and it was just grand. We married in 1953. It was a simple wedding with the Registrar. We went to Coupar to my auntie Kate's for a short honeymoon and it was lovely.

Alec: We lived with my mother-in-law and stayed in that house down the Ferry for twenty-eight years. Moving to Hilton in 1980 was my first house. When I came out of the army I worked for British Railway, then I worked in Thomson and Brown's in Castle Street. After a while I moved and got a job in Burnett's bakery slicing bread and was there for twenty years. Moving on my friend and I left and went to work in the Moray Firth Maltings where I stayed until I retired in 1993.

Jean: For holidays we used to go down to family in Fife. We never went abroad but we had good times and the children enjoyed it.

Alec: Every holiday my father would have jobs for me to do. I would say I didn't want to do anything because I was on holiday. He would insist, saying it would be money in my pocket and so I did. I worked on a farm and did whatever came up. Money was tight so it all helped.

Jean: At one point Alec was working up at Loch Luichart which meant he was away during the week and only home at weekends. Although that wasn't what we wanted, the pay was much better so it was the way it was.

Alec: I had a lovely garden at the house down the Ferry and I grew everything – beetroot, cabbage, turnips, potatoes, carrots, and kale. The soil was perfect for growing not like where I am now, the soil is really bad – I can't grow anything. I remember my next door neighbour asking, "Can I have some beetroot." She offered to boil it and jar it for me." There was great community spirit in the Merkinch area. Times were hard for folk and money scarce and so people helped each other. One neighbour may have made a pan of soup and they would then share it with their neighbours. A lot of that kindness and support happened all the time. People trusted each other, for example you never thought to lock your doors, and people freely called in on each other to offer help and friendship.

Jean: In those days Grant Street was great for doing the shopping. There was everything in the one street such as the Co-operative, a shoe maker, the Post Office, three butchers, a furniture shop, Stevie Fraser's shop where he just sold milk. Where Nicol's is now there used to be a grocers and it was one of the last shops in Inverness that sold butter in slabs where you could choose how much you wanted and it would be cut and wrapped in paper. We had an account with one grocer where I could get shopping on a daily basis and go in at the end of the week to pay it off. Shopping would be wrapped in brown paper and tied with string. The reason for using brown paper is that it stopped food going mouldy! We also had Bob's shop down the ferry which was a grocer shop but really it sold everything and it was much cheaper than the shops in Grant Street.

There was also the Grant Street Hall (I think it is now known as the Welfare Hall) where boxing and dances were held. It was a great place. Grant Street was a lovely place, I just loved it. The Ferry was nice but if folk asked where I came home I was always pleased to say I came from Grant Street!

Alec: There was a wee house which the children passed on their way to school with a brick in the wall where, when you passed, you were supposed to touch it for good luck.

Jean: There was also the football club - the Clachnacuddin Club - which is still there today. There was also the football social club which was a great place to go. There was also lots going on such as Bingo, social nights, and what we know call karaoke nights. A big change I think is that no-one from the council comes round and checks that your house is being kept in good order. Years ago, every so often someone would come in and check the garden was tidy and the walls were in good repair. They would list what you had to do and the come back and inspect the work had been done. It encouraged folk to take pride in their homes and then if they moved out and someone else moved in they could move in fairly quickly which is not always the same today.

Alec: When I was growing up we never stayed in one place for any length of time which meant I didn't set down roots. So when our family came along I decided I wanted them to have friends and a feeling of belonging so I was happy to settle here. We have had some really great times in the Ferry.

Jean: I would never leave Inverness. I was brought up here and there is a pull and longing to remain here.

6. Hannah Anderson

I was born in 1932 at Bell-Vue Farm just outside Muir of Ord opposite the grounds of the Black Isle Show. I lived with my mother and grandparents. My grandfather worked on the farm. We moved all over the place so I don't remember much about the early days. I do remember when I was three or four being given a Mickey Mouse tin tea set. Oh boy was I pleased with it! However, one night I left it outside and it rained so it got rusty and that was the end of that. I enjoyed playing skipping, rounders, cricket, houses and I had a teddy bear.

I started school at the age of five at Jemimaville where I was for six months. However, I contracted meningitis and polio so I was off school for a year and a half. The hospital wanted to take me down to Edinburgh and put me in an iron lung, but my doctor said if they moved me I would die. I was in a coma for six months and my legs were paralysed. Two specialists from Edinburgh came to see me. I remember waking up and at the bottom of the bed was Dr Anderson and the two specialists all looking at me. My granny had to rub my legs with olive oil and massage them and I had to learn to walk all over again.

I remember when living in Jemimaville it was the coronation of George VI in 1937 and all the children in the school were given a mug. They had a big 'do' in the village and we had games and everything.

We then moved to Balavaird Farm just outside Muir of Ord and I went back to school when I was seven. War had just started. My mum took me to school the first day on her bike and I remember wondering, "Oh I wonder if the Germans are going to get me."

There was no school dinner or bottles of milk, so I used to take a 'piece'. I took a tin flask with a wee handle on the side and with cocoa in it. Every classroom had a fire which was the only heating and the teacher would put everyone's flasks in front of it to heat it and then you would get it at break time. I remember it would be hot and burn my mouth! The school is where the Muir of Ord art class meet now which I attend every Saturday.

I had to go to church each Sunday and I wasn't allowed out to play afterwards. I could go for a walk as long as I was quiet but that was about it. I wasn't allowed to play cards. I would get told "if you touch those cards I will break your fingers!!" It was boring. I went to church and we would walk along the railway to East Church in Muir of Ord which was about a mile each way.

The day we moved in my granddad was diagnosed with T.B. and was put in a sanatorium where he later died. There was no cure for T.B. in those days.

At twelve, children who passed their Eleven Plus test went to Dingwall Academy. Those who didn't pass stayed in primary school. I didn't go to the Academy because my grandfather had died, mum was married and away and it was just me and granny. She was sick and I had so much time off school to look after her. I clearly remember my teacher, Miss Mackenzie. She only had one class because it was considered the 'unimportant class'. She said to me "Just come when you can even if it is only for an hour or so because you are missing out on so much schooling." She was just wonderful.

When granny died I moved up to Newmore Croft at Mulbuie with my mother and step-father. He had to go away and get work because the croft didn't give us much money. I stayed home and did whatever needed doing on the croft. There was no running water. We had a twenty foot deep well and you had to drop down the pail on a rope to collect the water. In the summer it would go dry and we had a cart with a whisky keg and a lid on the top and a tap at the side. We would take a Clydesdale horse and cart with a whisky barrel on it and fill it with water from a spring well that never ran dry, about a mile away. It was very hard work and so we never wasted a drop of water. We had a coal fire, several rooms and one special room which was never used; it was kept nice in case the minister visited! As children we had a bath in front of the fire in a tin bath. When you grew up you just had a wash and kept yourself clean.

When I was a kid, a baker's van from Beauly came round twice a week each Wednesday and Saturday. A butcher's van and a grocer's van came round every Friday and you bought your shopping using your ration book. There were Hays, Lipton, and the Co-op. They weren't supermarkets as we know now, they were just shops. During the war we were lucky because we could get milk from the farm twice a day. Granny had hens so we had plenty of eggs. Indians were stationed in the Muir and they had mules which they exercised along the country roads. They could be seen for miles - just lines of mules. One of the Indian men would come up to granny and ask her for a dozen eggs. In return he would give her a hankie full of tea because it was rationed. Now that was Black Market!!

We might have a bit of beef if we were lucky. Sometimes we had stewed rabbit, and if I got a sausage, I was well pleased. I remember Saturday nights I always got a pie. That was what I liked the best because I would have brose for breakfast. At dinner, when I was at school, I would have my 'piece' and in the evening I would have whatever the rest of the family had: usually a bowl of soup, or perhaps fried tatties. I had porridge every day - five days a week. My grandfather would only have it one way, which meant It would be all lumpy and I used to hate it but I was told, "If you don't eat it you will have it for breakfast." I had been busy at school or working all day. I walked all the way home and sat down to eat and then I was expected to eat a bowl of lumpy porridge. I didn't like it at all.

When I lived at the croft I had a pony and trap – a Governess cart - which I used when I went to collect the messages. One day Snowy, my pony, got a fright and she took off. She was going so fast she couldn't take the corner, straight across the road she went and we landed in the field. Snowy went down on her front legs. I thought she had broken them but she was shaking and the messages were scattered everywhere. So we set off home again.

When we were living at the croft we would go to The Black Isle Show. At that time it didn't have its own ground like it does today. Farmers would take turns to have it on their farm. I remember one time; I was presenting Snowy with the Governess cart and I was awarded Highly Commended. I was quite chuffed. I really loved Snowy.

I used to listen to a programme on the radio every night at a 6:45pm – 'Dick Barton, Special Agent' and he had two side-kicks, Jock and Snowy, and I loved that programme so I called my pony Snowy after his namesake from the programme.

The radio was a battery radio. We had no electricity at the croft so we had a big battery and what was called a wet-battery which we had charged up at Nobles shop in the village for sixpence. You would drop it off and then pick it up. If the battery got low when Dick Barton was on I would get down on my knees, ear pressed against the radio to hear it. Our collie dog would come and lie over my legs and I never felt the dog till the programme was over, and I would think "Oh my legs!"

I got a job looking after our neighbour's wife who was sick. I used to do the heavy work and got £1 a week wage and would send half of it home. After that I went down to Milngavie at the age of fourteen as an under-nanny. When I arrived the nanny was sick so I got left with everything. This was fine because I had four brothers and three sisters, and as the eldest I was used to looking after bairns. I didn't stay there long because I was so homesick. We still had rationing and as I was under sixteen I had a green ration book which meant I could get bananas. The lady of the house used to get them for me. After that I came home and got a job in Beauly in the Taj Mahal which was a fish and chip shop, and that is where I met my husband Robbie. He came into the shop to see his sister and get some free chips. He was playing in the Dominoes Club representing Inverness and came in to play Beauly. I was about seventeen. I worked six days a week from 10am to 10pm every day and it was hard going. I only had Mondays off and who went out on a Monday? So I didn't see much of Robbie then. We eventually met up again when I was about twenty. We didn't have telephones then so communication was by letter.

We would go to the pictures in Inverness and go dancing in the local hall. I remember Robert Wilson was the Voice of Scotland and I loved him and Scottish music. One time he came to the Empire Theatre and so one night I took Robbie to see Robert Wilson and Robbie has loved it ever since. The doorman at the La Scala was an old WW1 veteran and he would stand there complete in his full uniform with his row of medals. We were convinced they were chocolate medals!

When we went out to the pictures we went into town on the bus. Nobody had cars then. By then I was working in Dingwall in Morgantis', an Italian café in the High Street where Boots is now. They did beautiful ice cream and people would come up from Glasgow for the ice cream. I would work from 9am to 6:30pm but each Wednesday and Saturday I worked from 9am to 10:30pm. It was a long day. I also had half day Thursday. I got £2.5/- a week when I started and I was there four years. By the end I got £3.00. I used to give £1 to my mother and then I had my bus fare and clothes etc. to get with the rest.

We got married when I was twenty-two in East Church in Muir of Ord and had our reception in the Ord Arms Hotel with a hundred people at it. The car came for me and there were no ribbons on it. My mother said, "You know fine it is a bridal car so where is the ribbon? Do the job properly and go get the ribbons." She liked everything done properly so they went back to Muir and got the ribbons, as a result I was twenty minutes late!

There was a Polish man lodging with Robbie's mum and he loaned us his car to drive us from the reception into Inverness where we got the train to Aberdeen where we stayed in the Bon Accord Hotel for a week. We returned and went to live with Robbie's sister in a room in Laurel Avenue in Inverness.

We had each both saved up 10/- a week and put it in the new TSB Dingwall. We had £50 when we got married. In our first home we had a lovely bed settee suite – mum got it for us and it cost £40. We bought a sideboard and dining room suite with a drop down leaf because when the bed was down you couldn't have the table up and vice versa. We agreed to buy things one at a time as we could afford it and we have done that all our lives. When we lived in Inverness I got a job in Duncan Fraser's chip shop and got £4.00 a week. Robbie worked in a warehouse for SPD Lever Brothers going round delivering Sunlight soap, cooking fat and soap powder.

Then in 1956 we decided to go off to New Zealand. We saved £100 which covered Robbie's fare. He went out first and I followed six months later. I left Inverness at eight in the morning and travelled down to London on the steam train, arriving at eleven o'clock at night. I stayed in the Euston Hotel then the next day caught the boat train to Southampton. I boarded a fairly new boat called the 'Southern Cross' and set sail for our new life in New Zealand.

I was on the boat for six weeks. I was in a six berth cabin. There were four English girls and one girl from Aberdeen who I chummed up with. There was a lovely library and so I read all the books they had on Robert Burns from the start to end of his life. The ship arrived in January which of course was summer time. We rented a house for three years and then built our own place. While there, I worked in a place making trousers. We lived there for twenty-three years and had our four sons. However, we were still homesick and returned to Newmore Croft in 1979 where we lived for six months before moving into the street we are in now. I got a job in the café in Muir of Ord and worked there for sixteen years.

I am now long retired and still happily living in Muir of Ord. I am involved in my local church and a founder member of the Muir of Ord art class. As I said, I have travelled and lived in different places, but for me there is no-where like home.

7. Peter Chisholm

I was born in 1930 in Inverness Castle. The castle was built in two parts; one was the prison and the other the Sherriff Court. When they opened Porterfield prison in 1902 that part in the castle was no longer needed and became the headquarters of the Inverness County Police where my father worked. There were two flats in the castle, one for the caretaker and one for police use. I lived there for six months then we moved to a council house in Macewen Drive. We had all 'mod-cons' such as hot water and a full bathroom. We lived there for six years before moving to Bellfield Park in 1936 into our old - stone house which cost £600.

I started school when I was six and went to Notre Dame Convent School which was located in a big house next to what is now St Ninian's Catholic Church. I went there for three years and then went to Inverness Royal Academy (IRA) primary school which at that time was on the same site as the Academy. School lunches were not provided. I would go home. Children who came in from the country would stay in school and have their packed lunch.

I cycled every day which took me about ten minutes. In primary school there was no uniform apart from a tie. By the time I was in secondary school the war had broken out and so it was difficult to get uniforms and using coupons for school uniforms was not an option. Clothing, as well as food, was strictly rationed.

I remember when I was in Primary 6, being told off most severely one day by my teacher for wandering back into school at three o'clock. On my way back to school at lunchtime I had

46

stopped off to watch a house fire. "You should have been here at two o'clock," she said. I was quite indignant. The funny thing is I remember the fire but I don't remember what I did in school that day!

A big highlight for me was Bertram Mills Circus coming to Inverness in 1938. The Suspension Bridge had been condemned for some unknown reason and the weight restriction was limited. The circus elephants had to walk down the riverside, across the Black Bridge and come up the other side of the river. I have always had a soft spot for elephants so I would go over to Bught Park every morning and watch them being brought down to the river for a bath. I was absolutely intrigued. They also had a Fakir called Koringa who hypnotised crocodiles. She had steps made of swords which she walked up as well as laying on a bed of nails. An exotic creature and the first person I had ever seen from another ethnic origin.

As a child we didn't have many family holidays. One trip I remember was when we went to Dundee to see my mother's sister. We travelled by train and I remember between Perth and Dundee we were in a carriage to ourselves. Two of my older sisters, whom I didn't see much of because they were away at boarding school, seemed to appear at holiday times and as a result I thought of them as aunts. One of them had a pair of gloves and when no-one was looking I threw them out the window. What a search went on for these gloves and needless to say I never told them what happened to them!!

From about eleven years old each summer I would cycle to Arisaig, which was approximately ninety-seven miles, to relations for my holidays to their croft. I would cycle to Fort William the first day, then forty miles onto Arisaig the next day. This was during the war and through a restricted area.

You had to have a permit to get in unless you were under twelve years of age. It was a Commando training area and as a result there were soldiers everywhere. In fact there were areas north of Inverness which were also restricted and were military and Commando training areas. For example, there was a barrier just over the Lovat Bridge. You could go straight across to Strathglass but you could not get into Beauly unless you had some form of identification or permit.

While waiting for my National Service call-up, I kept getting student deferments and sat my Highers twice. In the Inverness Royal Academy there was, in my opinion, a rotten maths teacher known as Parrot. She was small in stature and had a beak nose which is where her nickname came from. However, in fourth year I had a great teacher and I went from being unable to add 2+2 together to doing my Lower and then Higher Maths the following year. During the war there were very few male teachers, schools had to rely on retired women teachers - to me some of them seemed very old and past their sell by date!

The most enjoyable part of my schooldays started at 4pm every day. Between Evan, my lifelong friend, Hughy Williamson and myself, we were captain and vice captains of the rifle club, shinty club, rugby, hockey, badminton, cricket and country dancing. You name it we were in it. All of which were run in school. Some people have frowned at the rifle club – pointing .22 rifles at a target in the gymnasium with no ear mufflers, or warning signs on the door not to come in. We had targets pinned on two or three railway sleepers at the end of the room. But it wasn't only there. My first badge in the Scouts was my Marksman badge. I suppose such activities were encouraged as we were next in line for the Armed Forces.

There was a large poster in school showing how to overcome and disable a German parachutist should one drop in!

We always had our family meals together. My father was very senior in the Police Force and was on call all the time. As a result we had three telephones in our house which was very unusual as most people didn't even have one. We had two outside lines and one direct line to Police Headquarters. My father was also a great gardener and grew both vegetables and fruit and we also had hens and during rationing we got hen meal. North of the Caledonian Canal there was no egg rationing at all. We had a neighbour from Caithness and my parents would get so many dozen eggs from them and we would preserve them in some liquid stuff called waterglass in a large crock. When they floated in this liquid we knew they had gone off. My mother's side of the family were game-keepers and so sometimes we would get venison or pheasants and we also had plenty of fish – that was not rationed! Kessock herring was very popular and cheap. In May we would cycle to Loch Ashie for gull eggs. Black headed gulls nested there in their hundreds.

I had lots of interests such as fishing, marbles, conkers, and ice skating in Loch Na Sanais which is now reduced in size and in the middle of Torvean Golf Course. It was comparatively shallow and froze quickly. We had hard winters in those days and it was used by the whole town. The current ice rink followed many years later. In fact I remember one day I fell through the ice when wearing my kilt. I fell in waist deep. I got out, ran all the way home and by the time I got there my kilt was stiff and my knees cut with the ice. My mother said, "Take all that off and get a hot bath." Next she said, "Oh wait a minute, you need to light the stove first and heat the water." By the time I got the bath I could have died of pneumonia!!

49

I also attended the Outdoor Club at the Academy. We would be out every weekend walking the Munros and hostelling. A typical long weekend would be Friday night cycle to Strathpeffer, Saturday up to Carbisdale Castle Youth Hostel, (Golspie) Castle; Sunday over to Ullapool and Monday back to Inverness.

There were several grocer type shops around and smaller shops that would have basic items. One was Hettie's at the top of Castle Street. From time to time my mother would send me up there to get a loaf – a wrapped loaf because Hettie's cat sat in the window and had free range of the shop! Also there was one lady who sold sweets from the window of her house. You just knocked on her window and she would sell her sweets. No health and safety regulations then!

When I was eleven I got a Saturday job delivering meat for a butcher. The Tattie Holidays held each October was a key part of the year. The aim was for the children to help with the harvesting so they would work on farms. An alternative was the Forestry Commission which I did from the age of twelve to fourteen. The minimum age for working for the Forestry was fourteen but they needed all the help they could get so they turned a blind eye to age. Remember during the war, the only forestry workers were old men and boys. They gave me a curved saw which was fixed to the end of a four foot pole and I had to cut the branches off young pine trees, up to six or seven feet. This was to ensure the trees grew straight. This was called 'shedding'. I was also shown how to plant, weed and general maintenance.

As a Christian household, Christmas was always a big day. The town was not disposed to it being a holiday. It was considered a normal working day. I did three years delivering the Christmas post and on Christmas Day I took the first delivery and then the permanent postman would do the second so he could get his tips. I remember one Christmas I was over in Dalneigh and I was at my last house when the lady of the house said, "Hold on a minute son," and she came back with two hot mince pies – that was the best tip I got!

I remember my friend David; his parents had the Fashion Salon in Union Street and they needed a parcel delivered to Fortrose, so the pair of us took the parcel by bicycle. This meant catching the ferry. When we got there the lady offered some tea, boiled eggs and scones which were delicious. I think we must have taken too long over them because we got back to North Kessock at 9:30pm and the last ferry had just gone. We shouted but it made no difference, so we had to cycle through Redcastle up to Muir of Ord, onto Beauly and round and back to Inverness. We only had 6^d between us so I used 3^d to phone to tell my folks we were both safe and the other 3^d we used to buy a bag of chips to share between us. It must have taken us about three hours to get back to Inverness that night.

When I was seventeen I went to work at the filling station at Delmore on the road to Beauly (where Mitchell's Motor Cycles are today). I was left in charge. Years later a school friend told me that when he would come to see me while I was serving petrol he used to help himself to the chocolate and sweets! I probably got the blame! I didn't know one end of a car from the other. Although food rationing was easing, petrol was still in short supply so coupons were still in place for petrol. I was supposed to collect them when I filled up customer's cars - there was no self-service then. One delivery day a big tanker came in with 5000 gallons of petrol. The driver asked, "Do you want to dip the tank first." I asked "Why?" He said "To make sure that I am giving you the 5000 gallons." So I did. Then when he had finished filling up he asked if I wanted to dip the tank again. Again I asked "Why?" To which he replied, "To make sure you got all the petrol you have asked for!" I could have ruined that place financially! I worked there five and a half days a week.

That was 1947 and there were still a lot of Italian POWs in the area. Every morning they would be brought out and dropped off to work on the various farms round about and then they would be picked up at the end of the day. They wore British Army uniforms with big yellow and red patches on them to identify them as a POW.

I did my National Service from 1949-1951 and was mainly based in Catterick in Yorkshire, Norfolk and Dorset. I was due out October 1951 and around that time the regiment were sent out to Korea but thankfully I didn't have to go. I was a tank fitter and just after they arrived they lost a tank to the North Koreans or Chinese and some men were killed too. I then spent a compulsory three years in the Territorial Army with the Queen's Own Cameron Highlanders. As 'part-time' soldiers this meant two evenings a week at the Cameron Barracks, Sundays at Fort George firing ranges and an annual two week camp down in the Borders. This latter time off was given by my employer in addition to my normal holiday entitlement.

When I eventually returned from the Army I answered an advert to work for a large insurance company and stayed there until I retired. Every promotion I received meant a move elsewhere so I ended up living in various places around the UK.

My wife was from Inverness. We met through the church. I was in the church choir and she was the organist. She was very sporty, a great swimmer, better than ever I was. She was also an expert badminton player and was Ladies Singles Champion for the Under 18s in the North of Scotland. Her sister lived in Glebe Street and was the key holder for the old swimming pool. Often, when it was closed to the public my wife and sister would spend half the night swimming in the empty pool.

We married in 1955. We had a week's honeymoon in Edinburgh. My father-in-law worked for the railway and back then the train had carriages with six seater self-contained compartments. So he booked two compartments on one of the carriages and we jumped on, waved goodbye to everyone, shook off all the confetti and then moved into the next booked compartment.

As I mentioned, through my work we lived in various places, but it was always our intention to end up back in Inverness. My wife didn't have particularly good health and so I retired a year early so I could look after her and returned home to Inverness. I think one of the biggest changes in Inverness is in the architecture and sadly the centre of the town is no longer the hub that it was. Having said that, for me the thing I like about Inverness is that it is home. The river and the hills never change.

8. Joanna Cobham

I was born in 1930, nine years before war started and I lived in Gourock, Renfrewshire. During the war the area was heavily bombed and we spent long years waiting for the sirens to go off to warn us to grab our bundles of clothes and rush down to the shelter. It was so much part of life during those years. I often think how worried my mother must have been, and yet I don't remember being worried. I just accepted the banging.

As a child I loved playing 'peevers'. We would draw out squares on the pavement with chalk and then hop in and out of the squares. I also remember throwing a ball against the wall to various rhymes and actions. I read a lot, in fact I was never without books and I have always loved dolls. During the war years toys were hard to come by. I remember my mother's cousin Eva, who we stayed with when we came to Inverness; she never had a doll so when she was eighty I bought her one!

I started school in Gourock at the age of five and the name of my headmistress was Miss Barton. I walked to school every day which took ten to fifteen minutes. I remember walking along and across the bridge by the railway - never thinking of it as being unsafe. There was none of this driving you to and from school!

At twelve I went up to the High School in Gourock and stayed there until I was fifteen when I had to move to the High School in Greenock to finish my education.

In the nine years before the war, we as a family would go on outings across to Dunoon on the paddle steamer, or have a day out to Rothesay. However, when the war began in 1939, there was what was called the 'Boom' and you couldn't get out of the Clyde. The furthest you could go was Dunoon, and so as a family we would come up to Inverness for a couple of weeks. I would stay with my mother's cousin Aunt Eva in a two bedroom house and kitchen. I would sleep in the kitchen on a camp bed. It was great because it didn't matter to Aunt Eva how many people came - the rule was you just rolled over and let the next person in. I think that was what I loved about it - everything was so relaxed and easy.

My mother's aunt and uncle lived up in Alness and on occasions we would visit them. I was about ten or eleven and thought this was torture. They had no electricity or running water. The water had to be collected from the nearby burn. When travelling to Invergordon from Inverness my mother had to show her ID card - you weren't allowed to go north of Inverness without it.

At the beginning of the war, like everyone else, we were issued with gas masks which came in a small cardboard box and you were expected to take it with you everywhere. Now-a-days it seems to be necessary to have the latest mobile phone or trainers. At that time our only form of one-up-man-ship was the latest design in gas mask container!

When we travelled to Inverness it would be either on the train or the bus. The bus had wooden seats, and it took ages - about six hours from Glasgow because there was no A9 as we now know it. So we would go through all the little places on route. It was so tedious, dead slow and stop! I remember counting the mile stones as we approached Inverness. I recall one occasion we stopped somewhere for a cup of tea and behind us there was a black American soldier. Now you didn't see black people in those days at all, but out of all the people on the bus he was the only person to get my mother a cup of tea and to help her.

I have always loved travelling. Around 1947/48, just before I was eighteen, I went on my own to Germany for a month to stay with relations. At the London railway station there was a blue train, a red train and a green train. The blue one was for the British, the green one for the Americans and the red was for the Russians. It was quite frightening.

In Germany at that time 'cold perms' were popular and I had one. It cost me 5/-. In Britain, we did not have cold perms. To curl hair we would wind the hair round a small rod and wires which connected to a machine like today's hair dryers. Another amazing thing was they had wheelie bins, something we didn't get until fairly recently in Inverness. They had things we didn't even know about!

Housing has changed quite a lot in my time. As a child we had a range in the kitchen and a sink and bunker where we kept the coal. We also had what is called recess beds. There were two beds in both the living room and sitting room. These beds had doors across them, so when not being used they were hidden away. My parents, brother and I slept in one room together during the war.

There were nine tenants in the flats and we were number three. We all had to take turns in cleaning the stairs using pipe clay. I had to take my turn but thankfully in time my mother got someone to do it for us.

The fire in the kitchen heated the water in a tank up in the corner. When you heard the water gurgling you knew it was ready and you could have a bath. However, coal was needed to heat the water and it was scarce so you couldn't have a bath every day.

I have always loved Inverness and still do. In fact I moved to Edinburgh around 1992 to be near my family but after four years I returned to civilisation! It is so peaceful and I actually think the reason I love it so much is the connection with friends. One of them I am still friends with today - Jackie. He sends me a Valentine card every year without fail.

Would I rather be anywhere else? No! As I said, I love Inverness, I always have. I always will.

9. Heather Steel

I was born in 1931 in Hounslow, West London, which used to be part of Middlesex, now part of Greater London. I lived there with my parents and two sisters until 1954 when I moved to Southern Rhodesia, Africa, as it was known then.

In Hounslow we lived in a Victorian terrace which had three bedrooms, two living rooms and kitchen downstairs - no bathroom. The toilet was attached to the house but the entrance was outside. When very young we used to have a bath in the kitchen, but as we got older my sister and I used to go to the public baths every Saturday where we used the 'slipper baths'. These were proper baths that the public used for bathing. My parents didn't have a bathroom in the house until sometime after 1954.

I went to Spring Grove House Secondary School. It originally belonged to botanist Joseph Banks who sailed with Captain Cook in 1768. During his voyages he brought back specimens of plants and trees and planted them in the grounds. After him, and prior to it becoming Spring Grove School, it was owned by Andrew Pears, owner of Pears Soap.

My father was in the Army during the war. First he went to Norway, onto North Africa and then worked his way through Italy. He had been in the Territorial Army. In fact he was at Army camp in Bude, Cornwall when war was declared and he was immediately mobilised. As a result he was away most of my childhood. My mother worked in London for a while then in an Army Pay Office in Hounslow. We used to go up to town to the theatre regularly and would be taken to the famous Lyons Corner House - a special treat. Dad came home in 1945.

As children, for breakfast we had porridge in winter even in England! At weekends we used to have Sunday roast. Every Saturday my friend and I used to go swimming and then first thing on Sunday morning my sister and I went swimming. My father would come if he was home from his shift. My mother would have breakfast ready for us when we got home and then have Sunday lunch. She would then make a marvellous tea and all our friends would come. I never cooked before I was married. Because my mother was such a good cook, I never had to, so I had to learn the hard way. But I loved it and still do.

As a child I was fortunate, I did have holidays. We went two or three times to the Isle of Wight to a Warner Holiday camp. At weekends it seemed to be good weather and we would get on the bus and go to Runnymede, Richmond and Marble Hill near the Thames and have picnics. Likewise, we attended day school and Sunday school picnics. We also travelled to Aberdeen to visit my grandparents.

We didn't have a television so we made our own entertainment. We used to go Scottish dancing – my father was an Aberdonian who was keen on dancing. A girlfriend from school and I went to dances at weekends. When we went dancing we invariably ended up walking home because the buses stopped running at 10:30pm.

We used to wear a nice outfit, something 'dressy'. I wouldn't wear trousers to go out, except for holidays. My sister would make her own long dresses. I made a long skirt and then had different tops. We used to get a nice dress at Christmas time. Eventually my parents also joined our dance group and my dad became chairman of the Heston and District Scottish Dancing

Association. They used to hold regular dances with special ones to celebrate big events such as New Year and St Andrew's Day.

I was an inveterate film fan. In Hounslow we had five cinemas from which to choose. A girlfriend and I would go to the cinema at least once a week. When I was small I used to belong to a film club and we used to go to the cinema each Saturday morning. As I got older we would go to see all sorts of films, such as war films or romances. I remember in 1948 being taken to the Odeon cinema next to the school to see Lawrence Olivier in Henry V.

During the '50s all the big American stars would come over and do a three week stint at the London Palladium which we would attend. I saw Frank Sinatra - my favourite, Judy Garland, Frankie Lane - all sorts of stars – all the stage musicals and I still have all the programmes.

In the '40s and '50s our entertainment was the cinema, dancing and once people started getting cars - treasure hunts.

On leaving school, my Headmaster wanted me to go to Cambridge University but I couldn't get in. I could have gone to London University but it would have meant being a day student travelling back and forward and that wasn't going to university as far as I was concerned. I really didn't know what I wanted to do. I would have liked to be a film continuity girl because I was such a film fan but you couldn't get into film work without a Union card and you couldn't get a Union card if you weren't working in films! So I went along to the 'Senior Mistresses Working Bureau'. She gave me an application form for the Foreign Office. I had an interview and got a job in the Foreign Office Intelligence Co-ordination Staff Department. I didn't work in Downing Street but worked in Broadway opposite. I really simply drifted into the Civil Service.

I worked from 10am - 6pm Monday to Friday which was good because it meant I missed the rush hour both ends. The office was directly across from St James' tube station and near St James' Park. In the summer we could sit in the park at lunch times or jump on the tube and go up to Oxford Street and look at the shops. When I was working in London I got home after 7pm so my mother would have a cooked tea ready for me. A new Passport Office was built just along the road from us. They had a far better canteen than ours so we used to go along there. In fact the girls and I in the office were the founder members of that canteen although we didn't even work for them!

Near to the office, in fact where New Scotland Yard is now situated, there used to be a Delicatessen. Yoghurts were a new thing back then and they used to sell different flavoured small pots every month so you could sample them.

I think we got a fortnight's holiday. I enjoyed my work and felt right in the centre of things. We were allowed out of the office to watch the parades in the Mall. Half would be allowed out to watch the parade go one way and then the other half to watch it come back. I remember clearly going with my parents to the Mall to see the Coronation Parade. As children and young people we were taken to all the Royal parades and special events. We had a great time.

Even though I worked in the Foreign Office I never got the chance to go abroad. My sister, a school teacher, had been to Rhodesia and we had lots of people from Rhodesia visit the family home during the war. So I went to Rhodesia House,

61

which was in the Strand in London, now known as Zimbabwe House, and asked them for a job. They said they couldn't offer me a job immediately, but if I made my own way to Rhodesia they would guarantee me a job on arrival; so that is what I did.

I went by Union Castle Steamer from Southampton to Cape Town, South Africa. It took two weeks. Then four days in a steam train to Rhodesia. On arrival I lived in a Government hostel just outside the capital city - Salisbury, now known as Harare. It had been an RAF camp with only huts for accommodation. I arrived in July 1954.

I got a job in the Governor's office in Southern Rhodesia. I then moved to the Department of Justice. Eventually I moved to Northern Rhodesia and became the Passport Officer until I got married. In those days the Government didn't employ married women, so I did reception and typing work for a private company which sold fuel cookers, delivery of fuel and paints. The Scots owners were originally from Bonnybridge in Stirlingshire.

Jim arrived the following September. He was from Edinburgh and was a planner with the government. We started courting in 1955/56. One of the girls on the ship called Margaret came from Edinburgh and her room was opposite mine. Because Jim was from Edinburgh, he and another guy, also from Edinburgh, palled up and would go to Margaret's for a cup of tea. I ended up going for tea too and we then all used to go to the cinema, have picnics, attend rugby matches, and so the romance started.

During our courtship Jim was seconded to Northern Rhodesia now known as Zambia. I followed shortly after and we got married there in 1957. My parents came out from the UK for the wedding. My father was working for the airline BOAC at the time so he got concessionary fares. For our honeymoon we had a long weekend in a local hotel that had been taken over by some Chinese owners. Again we lived in a Government hostel in Northern Rhodesia for a while.

However, we decided it was time to come home and so on Christmas Eve 1959 we sailed to Southampton complete with a car and dog. When we docked the dog was taken into quarantine and we were trying to get the paperwork done so we could get the car. Most of the officials had gone home so we were told we would have to wait until after Christmas to get the car. Jim said that was not acceptable. In the end, we promised to return after Christmas to sort out the paper work, which he did, and we then drove off to Hounslow to stay with my family for Christmas. After the holiday we drove up to Edinburgh to Jim's parents' home where we stayed until October 1960. I got a job in Edinburgh as Assistant to the Work Study Engineer at Alexander Cowan (Papermakers).

Jim had previously worked for West Lothian County Council and they had contacted him stating that if he was coming home they could guarantee him a job. So we moved to a little village between Edinburgh and Glasgow called Torphichen, in West Lothian. It is the place where Mary of Guise, mother of Mary, Queen of Scots was married. It is very ancient. It is also the Headquarters of Knights of St John of Jerusalem. We lived right in the old town square.

My husband subsequently got a job as a partner in an architects and planning office in Glasgow. Sadly it did not work out, so we started to think about what to do next. Jim knew I liked cooking. I had been doing a catering course just for interest and he suggested running a B&B or something similar. I

63

really didn't want to move but he found a hotel up in Strathglass in the Highlands and so we moved there New Year 1980 and we stayed till 1985.

Our B&B became a hotel where we offered evening meals and we had a bar which Jim managed as well as the large grounds. I really enjoyed it. The scenery around it was, and still is, beautiful. We used to get people that came for fishing and shooting. It was interesting and although it was hard work but it was also great fun.

We moved into Inverness and 'officially' retired in 1985. However, Jim then set up his own consultancy Town Planning business doing appeals for people. After that he opened a portacabin in the station car park where he sold his watercolour paintings and did the framing. When Rose Car Park took over, he moved out and he went round the streets in Inverness where he would sit and paint.

I saw an advert for Christmas staff in Boots. I applied and got the job over the Christmas period. Then, in the February, they contacted me again and asked me to go back and work part time which I did for quite a while. When we did finally retire we would go swimming, attend keep fit and Scottish Slimmers. I used to do a lot of knitting. In fact I knitted for a knitting designer who lived up in Glenmoriston who also had a shop in Beauly.

As had been our custom in Rhodesia, we preferred eating out in the evenings and we continued that when we came to Scotland. We would go out in the weekends to different restaurants - Italian or Spanish. As a result we made lots of friends from all over the world which in turn led to us going abroad on holiday.

10. Ali & Sandra Geddes

Ali: I was born in 1932 in Inverness. As a boy I went to Central Primary school. I walked to school. In fact we walked everywhere and you didn't really go out of town. Occasionally, my brother and I visited my grandparents who lived up in Invergordon. We always travelled to them by train.

I moved from primary school to the High School which I left at the age of fifteen. I felt the school wasn't really interested in me as an individual. It was just a matter of getting you in and getting you out, unless you were exceptional. Otherwise you were just 'run-of-the-mill'. So when I could I just left. They didn't even say 'Cheerio' or anything. I just left and didn't go back.

I remember we used to play 'kick-the-can'. We would get an old can and see how far you could kick it. Another thing we used to do was to go fishing down in the river or up at the canal. We would catch an eel or two and take them up to the fish and chip shop called Serafini's, run by some Italians in Young Street trading the eels for a bag of chips.

Down at Friars Shott there used to be two rowing boats. The guys with the boats would take their nets across the river and catch the salmon. They used to land them there and my pals and I would stand and watch them for ages. Going up the canal, there was bit known as Sandy Brae and we would slide down the brae, pick the berries and take them home to our mums to make jam.

Young people tended to be involved in something like Boys Brigade or Scouts and attended different activities two or three evenings a week in addition to the main meeting night.

We generally had porridge and always toast for breakfast. We had rabbit and also ate herring soaked in vinegar or oatmeal if we caught one. The milkman had a metal churn with both a a half-pint and a pint measure, so you would go out to the cart with your jug and get however much you wanted. At Christmas time we would have chicken and Christmas pudding. We had rice pudding or sponge and custard on week days.

Sandra: I was born in Nairn in 1934. I started Delnies Primary School at the age of five and would walk to and from there every day. When I was twelve I transferred to Nairn Academy which I cycled to every day - about four miles each way.

As a child, I remember we used to play 'houses'. We lived near a wood and we would collect the needles from the trees, put them into wee ridges to make lines for the different rooms and had a tin can and some string for a telephone. We would play with a ball and 'beddies' using a 'skitchie'. We also enjoyed a game of marbles or rounders, and of course, skipping.

My family loved singing. When our lessons were done we would have a sing-song. I also recall I attended the Guides once a week where I did my badges. That meant undertaking various activities such as keep-fit, cooking, and various things that as girls we would need to be future housewives!

I always had a proper lunch - stew, mince and tatties and at tea time I would have something like toad in the hole, or bacon and egg - not big portions but I seemed to have two meals per day. When in the country I would go down to the farm which was half a mile away from the house and get the milk. We had a milk pail with a lid which held three to four pints and I would go down whenever we needed milk, which worked out about four or five times a week.

I remember getting a day off school because the King, Queen and Princess Margaret were coming up and we stood at the corner of Bank Street. I remember saying, "I'm not going to wave and shout. How un-lady like!" However, when the car came I was there along with the rest of the crowd cheering and waving.

When I left school at the age of fifteen I worked in Low's the Grocer in Nairn. Then in 1953 I changed jobs and started work in the Inverness grocers D Cameron & Co in Queensgate. I travelled to work on the bus from Nairn and the shop paid my fare. At this time I met Ali who was also working there. After we were married and living in Nairn, we would come through on the bus together.

I remember one day at work it was very cold and one girl suggested that the following day we all wore trousers. When we came in, the boss, said, "We will not have trousers tomorrow," and that was it! It was considered not appropriate! The girls who lived locally were sent home to get changed, the rest of us made sure we wore skirts the next day.

When working in the shop there were no automatic tills so I had to know the price of everything and then add up the total in my head or on a piece of paper. There was no putting it through a scanner or calculator.

Ali: One of my fond memories is when the Bertram Mills Circus came to town. They arrived by train and then paraded through town to Bught Park. It was great watching the animals walking past. I also remember getting a day off work for the Highland Show which was held at the Bught Park. The thing I remember most was the huge number of people that gathered - it was phenomenal and was a big event in town.

I started work in a small grocer's shop in Kenneth Street. It was a father-and-son business and I was the gofer. My first wage was 10/- for six days a week. I worked there until I was called up to do two years National Service in 1951/52. I was sent to Fort George for basic training which lasted twelve weeks and then I was sent to Berlin where I was for the rest of the time. I used to do guard duty at Spandau Prison which was where German war criminals such as Hess and Speer were held. At the end of my time I was sent back to Fort George for demob. About three months before demob the Korean War was raging and the 1st Battalion Black Watch soldiers were heading out there. I was asked if I wanted to sign up but I said, "No thanks," came home and started work at D Cameron & Co. grocers shop in Queensgate.

Sandra: Ali and I started courting in 1953 and we would spend our time going to the pictures - the Playhouse or La Scala, in Struther's Lane. We attended dances in the Caley Hotel on a Saturday night and we also enjoyed walking by the river.

We got married in 1956 at Nairn High Church, now known as St Ninians, and held our reception in the Windsor Hotel, Nairn. We went to Perth for our honeymoon for two weeks. One week in the hotel, the other at my sister's in Grantown-on-Spey. My honeymoon was the first time I stayed in a hotel. We paid for that holiday before we went. In fact we saved for everything. We never bought anything until we had the full

68

amount of money for it. The only thing we never paid for outright was our house.

I worked in the grocers until 1958 when I left work to look after my niece. Then I worked in a newsagent in Nairn for a while before moving to work for the same company Ali was working for AB Chalmers. I worked there in the office until 1969, when our son was born thirteen years after we were married. I became a stay-at-home mum until he was about seven.

Our first home was in Innes Street in Inverness where we had two rooms, shared a kitchen and a wee toilet. We lived there for just over a year. When I had lived at home we had electricity and heating, whereas when we married we had gas and a coal fire but no electricity. Then we got a flat back in Nairn still sharing a toilet but Ali made a wee kitchen on the stair landing. We lived there for three years while we saved our money and bought a house in Holm Mills, Inverness where we lived for fourteen years. After that we moved to Midmills Road. Our son was at school by this time and I had time on my hands so we moved to a bigger house and I started doing B&B which I ran for nineteen years.

I remember when we lived in Holm Mills we got a twin tub washing machine. We had a three bedroom house but could only afford to furnish two of them until we saved up.

Ali: I remember in particular our first Christmas at our home in Innes Street. I sat with a load of torch bulbs, a cable and put them all together. We both made lantern covers from crepe paper and I connected them to a car battery. I was so chuffed with myself lighting this Christmas tree with my car battery. They lasted from 1956 to 1959! In our home in Nairn we didn't have electricity but I had a friend who was an electrician. At that time if you bought a cooker, the Hydro Board would connect you up to the mains. So we bought a cooker, and the Hydro Board duly connected us and my friend wired the house for us.

Each year, we got two weeks annual holiday plus Christmas Day and two days off at New Year. I also got local bank holidays. The shop was opened six days a week from 9am-6pm every day apart from Wednesday which was 9am-1pm. At the end of the day every Saturday we had to clean everything ready for the following week.

In the grocers when working at the counter I was expected to wear a collar and tie and a white coat which was changed twice a week. If it got dirty before that I would have to change it. In 1957/58 I left the grocers and went to work for the wholesale grocer's AB Chalmers as a traveller. The warehouse was based where Marks and Spencer is now. When I went to Chalmers about the job, the manager said, "There is only one condition, our travellers wear a hat. So if you want the job, get yourself a hat." I got one and called it a pork pie hat. When I started, there weren't many cars, certainly I didn't have one, and so I used to go around the Inverness area on my bicycle. However, I also had to travel to Lochinver and Ullapool and on those occasions I had to make sure the boss was in the office so I could borrow his car to do my visits. I worked for Chalmers for thirty-eight years.

When I retired, we moved out to Balloch. Inverness has seen good changes and bad changes but then when you think of it that is no different from any other town.

Sandra: When I think about what we had when we started married life and what our son has, I realise it is a very different world.

11. Keith and Cath Martin

Cath: I was born at home in Brown Street in Merkinch in 1935. I am one of six children. I started Merkinch School when I was about four or five and lived down the Ferry in West Drive. I remember my sisters taking me to school and it was very dark as there were no street lights. We used to walk through the Carse which was a field, now a nature reserve, over the railway line to school. I came home every lunch time, all the way back for a cup of tea and jammy piece. I remember being glad to be leaving Merkinch School and going to the 'big' school otherwise known as the Technical High School. When I went to the High School I did cookery and sewing in the main but even to this day I can't thread a needle!

One day a lad in my class at Merkinch School, who is still a friend of ours today, stole the teacher's strap and ran out of school, over the Greig Street Bridge throwing it in the river. I don't remember what happened to him at school but I do know he became a social worker and then a vicar!

I played outside a lot of the time; I would jump off the Kessock Ferry boat and swim in the water. I used to go over to the dump which was on the other side of the Ferry and collect all the bits of broken glass and china. I loved that and used it when I played 'houses'. I would walk through Leafy Lane to the Canal where there were logs chained together and I would step on them across to the other side of the water. Then there were the Rockies, up above the bridge at Clachnaharry. I would spend all day there on a Sunday. As I walked through Clachnaharry I would knock on the window of a particular lady's house and she would sell me a wee bit of toffee.

There was a well there which had really cold water and people would come and take water for elderly people who were in hospital who had asked for some cold water from the Clachnaharry Well.

Living down at the Ferry, everyone kept their gardens very tidy and there was a great community spirit with people looking out for one another.

I remember coming home from school and having to go into the scullery and stamp the blankets with my feet to get the water out and then put everything through the wringer.

There was no such thing as a week's holiday for us. Instead we had day trips. I remember we would go to Elgin for the day, have something to eat in a restaurant where the waitress would come and serve us, and then we would get to go to the shop and buy something like a book for drawing. It was a big day!

I left school at fifteen and I went to work in the Co-operative in Lochalsh Road. There were four parts to the Co-op - the baker, dairy, butcher and grocery which also included the office. I worked in the office. I sat on a high seat and could see people coming and going. When people bought something they would either put their money or their tokens into a container which was tied to string and this would be sent over to me at the cash desk. I would log the amount against their number in the big ledger. And then on Friday night when their husbands had been paid they would come in and pay some off or clear the debt completely.

When I was seventeen I worked for a dentist in Academy Street - 'Allan and Robertson'. I had various tasks but the one I remember most was mixing the stuff for the fillings. I got training on the job and I was there until I got married. I loved it. I remember the tough men who worked on the Hydro Schemes would come in and wouldn't want gas, they just wanted it out. They probably had been for a drink first! On Monday we would get the young Brothers from Fort Augustus Abbey. We also dealt with royalty. When the Gloucesters came up to their summer place at Farr if they needed a dentist they would come into us.

I used to go dancing in the Northern Meeting Rooms. Once a month the big bands would come to the Caley Hotel and on a Thursday night I would queue to get tickets for that. I remember one night I didn't wear my glasses and my optician came up to me and said, "Catherine where are your glasses?" I only knew it was him because he came up close! I also went to St. Mark's Church of Scotland in Thornbush Road, now it is a big furniture place. I was a Sunday School teacher there and also went to the Youth Fellowship. One night a group of young people came down from Castle Street Baptist Church and then we were invited back to their place. Anyway, we went this night and we were amazed! All these young people got down on their knees to pray. We had never seen anything like it yet there was so much laughter and talent amongst them. So I thought I am going to come back to this place. One Saturday night I decided instead of going dancing I would go to a meeting at Castle Street. On my way there I heard my boss who had a 'smack' with another car on Merlewood Brae. Well while we were having tea at this meeting there was a young guy sitting in front of me and he was talking about the fact he had had a smack with Allan the dentist before the meeting. So I leant forward and said, "That is my boss you are talking

73

about." So he turned around and said, "Would you like to come tomorrow to Ach-An-Eas Nursing Home? We are going there to sing to the old people." Anyway at my church the following morning I told my best friends to come with me to Ach-An-Eas. They didn't want to come but I said I wouldn't be friends with them anymore unless they did! We went and that was the start of my friendship with Keith.

Keith: I was born in Nairobi, Kenya in 1932 but I was a sickly baby with 'Pyloric Stenosis' and so my mother brought me home to Inverness. It took three weeks to get home. Mother was told by a German doctor that because I was such a sick baby I would be buried at sea. She nursed me and here I am eighty one years later!

My father went to work in London and so we moved and lived in Kent. I started school there at the age of five. I remember my father sending me down to the shop on a Sunday for sweets. For a few pennies I got toffee Golly bars - four for a farthing!

When war broke out in 1939 my father sent my mother and the four children up to Inverness to her brothers who were coal merchants. We travelled up from London by train and I always remember my uncles had a breakfast ready for us and they had different colour egg cups and I was disappointed I didn't get the blue one!

I lived in St. Margaret's in MacAndrew's Brae (now Midmills Road) - it was a big house and as a result they had a man servant. In the late 1940s and early 1950s they hosted garden parties for the YMCA - one uncle was the president of the YMCA. Cath and I also had our engagement party there.

Soon after the outbreak of war we moved out to Lewiston, Drumnadrochit where my mother got a house until 1945. There was no running water but we got a bath in the big basin every Saturday night. I remember hearing after we moved out of the house in Kent, that the next door to us had been bombed, completely obliterated and the owner of the house was thrown out his window across the road, but he did survive.

During the war there were very few toys. We spent a lot of time in what we called the 'Cover' which were the woods near Lewiston which went down to Loch Ness. As a school boy I helped in the Lewiston shop and went round with Tom Fraser in his van to help him. I also helped the milkman. He had a running board on the side of the milk cart and I would stand on that and run in with the milk and back. I also spent time trotting behind 'Alex the Carrier' who carried the goods from Temple Pier to Drum to Lewiston when the boats came in with the coal and stuff and that is where I got the love for farming. I used to hoe the turnips for him.

At dusk, I would go out to the hills and catch rabbits. I would trap them against the fence and take them home live and put them in hutches. One time I had well over a dozen of them. Unfortunately some of them got out one night and they ate Alex the Carriers young turnip shoots. I was far from popular for that! In those days I wore tackety boots.

At seven I started off in the IRA Primary for a year, then when we went to live in Drumnadrochit where I attended the primary school and at the right time I moved on to Glen Urquhart School till second year. We then moved back into Inverness when the war ended and finished my schooling in the IRA. I was very involved in the football, rugby and long distance running. I was Abertarff Junior House Representative in the second XI and second XV. I went home for lunch because I lived fairly close. I lived in Victoria Drive which looks onto Millburn Academy. It was great; I could watch all the matches being played on the Millburn playing fields from my house.

I became a Christian at the age of fourteen which was to impact on the decisions I made throughout the rest of my life.

The thing I loved about school was Maths. I was good with figures. It was the only thing for which I ever got 100%. I left school at fifteen and-a-half. The only choice of career offered to me was the bank or the farm. I remember going to see the Rector and telling him I had got the opportunity to work on a farm. I couldn't sit behind a desk all day; I liked the open air life far too much.

I started off as a student on a dairy farm - Dell of Inshes where Tesco Inshes is now. We started at 3:30am. Milking was at 4am and 4pm which took an hour each time. In between I did various jobs on the farm, harvesting, working the horse using the horse drawn scuffler which was a drill that cleaned the weeds between the turnips. My wages were £1.8/- a week. I would give my mother 10/-, use 10/- to buy 'bib and brace' and then the 8/- for collections, sweets and a tithe. After a while I thought this was not the life for me, and then after a year I went on an exchange visit through the Young Farmers Club to Sweden. There were fifteen lads from all over Scotland who went out to Sweden. We were allocated to farms as were the lads who came over here. I worked with two lads from Aberdeenshire and didn't understand the Buchan twang but they were great lads. We went by ship. When I came back I went to work on a poultry farm.

In 1948 I went to work for Charlie Munro, Cantray Home Farm, Croy and I was a poultry student. My wages were £2.10/-. They hatched 20,000 chickens a week during the season. I stayed with my boss's mother until she died and then I moved into the Bothy. I travelled back and fore on my bike. I could do Dalgrambich Farm, Croy to Inverness in twenty-five minutes. Eventually I got a two stroke motorbike. It could go to the top of Tower Brae, but then conk out! I would have to push it for a couple of miles to Culloden Battlefield for instance, and then it started again! In 1950 I went to Agricultural College in Aberdeen for two years and then another year in Ayrshire and worked up through the ranks.

Cath and I started courting when we were about nineteen and twenty-two respectively and married at twenty-one and twenty-four. I used to use the boss' van when we went out on a date and I proposed to Cath on Valentine's Day 1956 at 11:50pm down at the Ferry in the van looking over at North Kessock and she said "Yes!"

Cath: We got married in September 1956 in Castle Street Baptist. I couldn't afford a dress but Keith's sister's best friend sent me her dress and I borrowed my best friend's locket. Keith's boss and his wife used to grow gladioli and often travelled down to London to the Chelsea Flower Shows and win prizes. As a result they gave us all the flowers for the church and made up the bouquets for my bridesmaids and me. They also gave us a bedroom suite as a wedding present. Each side of the bed we had wooden egg boxes as bedside cabinets and my sister draped material round them so they looked nice and we could put lamps on them.

77

Keith: We had our reception in the Columba Hotel, and there was no alcohol or dancing. One of the deacons in the church owned it and he was very good to me. It cost 10/- a head. He gave me time to pay it and he was very kind. We then went off down to Glasgow to start our honeymoon. We had my uncle's car so we went to Darlington, Blackpool, Morecambe, Scarborough and various places. We had nearly two weeks.

Cath: We came back up through Edinburgh and Keith phoned his boss to see if the house was ready. His boss said, "No don't come back yet the house is not ready." As a consequence, we had to stay for a bit longer in Edinburgh. I was desperate to get home, see everyone and get settled. I had never been away like this before and have hated Edinburgh ever since!!

I remember when we were first married we had to eat and sleep in this one room and share a bathroom. We had a tiny wee kitchen. We moved four times while living on Cantray Home Farm and three times since living in Inverness - now we are in a two bedroom flat at Inshes and we love it!

I did go back to work after I was married for six months. I worked for the Potato Marketing Board and then I became pregnant and so I was at home with my children. I had six children in eight years - must have been the eggs!! When we had the farm I worked part time but my priorities were the children and home.

Keith: After fifteen years working at Cantray Home Farm I went to look for some land and ended up at Hilton Farm (Hilton Court is there now) where we got advice from a farmer in a totally amazing way. We were going to stay in a caravan but we went to the house next door and they said they were renting it from Mr and Mrs McKinnon. We contacted them and they said that in fact they were planning to sell it to their son. However, in answer to prayer they phoned the poultry farm wanting to speak to me. Mrs McKinnon said "We haven't been able to sleep thinking about you and decided you can have the house."

We believe it was a miracle. We believe we have had many miracles down through the years as a result of our prayers.

We worked the farm for twenty-five years building it up from 4,800 birds to 25,000 birds. Our Farm shop sold things like groceries, vegetables, ice cream and sweets for the children, poultry round to Nairn and Inverness and a packing station - which was an egg grading station. We candled them, checking for blood spots, packed them and sold them to shops, dairies, hotels and such like around Inverness and Nairn during the tourist season. A lot of young people worked for us on Saturdays and school holidays over the years.

Things were beginning to get difficult especially when the Co-op opened their new shop where Inshes Tesco is now. I could buy beans in the Co-op cheaper than I could buy them from the wholesaler to retail in our shop. A number of people were trying to buy us out but I kept stalling. I felt we had an asset rather than a liability. Eventually we sold up - seven weeks before Edwina Curry starting talking about salmonella! The other amazing thing was there were changes in tax law and if we had sold when we were being pushed we would have lost the price of three bungalows. We were able to clear our feet which a lot of poultry farmers were not able to do. A lot of them went bankrupt all over Scotland. We were very thankful. In 1988 I retired and I got involved in driving for a garage. I would get the train down to London and while on the train I would write up the church minutes and then pick up ambulances etc. and drive them back North. I also helped Blythswood Charity taking aid to people in Eastern Europe immediately after the 1989 revolution. I did thirty-four trips and during that time I was employed by Blythswood as an Area Co-ordinator which involved speaking in schools and churches about the charity. I also negotiated the opening of new shops in different places including Inverness. Even though we are now getting older we are still very much involved in our church. I also passed my heavy goods vehicle licence at the age of fifty-nine!

Over the years we have given hospitality to numerous people including a 'moon walker' - Colonel Irwin, Astronaut on Apollo 15 shuttle, and his children at the Wester Culcabock Farm House in June 1979.

Cath: The biggest changes we have seen over the years have been the expansion of Inverness and the development of the retail parks.

Keith: For me, the biggest change is the fields I knew and worked on as a boy and as a young agriculture student now built on with houses and retail units and open on a Sunday. For us it is also sad to see churches that were once well attended, now struggling. But it is good to see there seems to be new places of worship springing up across the city.

Keith & Cath: We love living in Inverness. The friendliness and helpfulness of the people, the concern for one another, is so good. The freedom to worship without persecution is important to us and the peace and tranquillity, beauty spots and scenery close to and surrounding Inverness is second to none.

12. John and Anne Lyle

John: I was born in Nairn in 1934. I was a son of cattle and sheep farmer and had three siblings. From the age of five I walked three miles to school each day. During the war, Canadian soldiers were billeted in the area near the school and when cutting down timber they would allow us to jump on the back of the lorry and get a lift up to school.

I attended Nairn Academy, leaving school at the age of fifteen. It so happened that harvest started and the farm-hand had left. As a result I had to stay off school to help with the harvest and then I stayed off even longer and never went back to school!

My parents came from Glasgow where they had a farm. I think they were very brave leaving Glasgow and moving up to Inverness to take on the farm near Nairn in 1929.

We were never taken out much apart from Saturdays when we would all get in the car to Nairn where my brother and sisters and I would go into RS McColl shop where we would be taken round the counter to choose some sweets. This was our highlight! As a late teenager I would go with my father by car to the cattle market in Inverness on Tuesdays. We also went into Nairn on a Thursday afternoon to the Grain and Feed Market held in the street and where all the farming, tradesmen and sales people would meet and trade with each other.

Our neighbour in the next farm was a bachelor and would come round to our farm with his ferrets and we would go out into the fields and set the ferrets down the rabbit holes to

81

draw them out. We would then take the rabbits home for our tea.

My dad would also kill sheep, skin them and hang them in the barn and, as and when they were wanted, he would cut a slab off and mum would cook it. We had no fridge so the barn did the job. Of course, there were flies flying around but it didnae do any harm. Mum would make hare soup and guess what? The blood of the hare would be the stock for the soup. Overall we were self-sufficient. We used to soak the oatmeal the night before so it was ready for breakfast the next day. We would milk the cows and mother would churn the milk round and round making it into blocks of butter.

We didn't go on holiday. As a family, we would go down to Nairn beach most Sundays and spend the day there. On occasions, I would go with my mum on the steam train to Glasgow and then change trains to Bishopbriggs to see my granny. Because of the distance we didn't see relatives that often. However, I do remember when I was about sixteen going down to Milngavie to see cousins and we went and played golf. My first 'real' holiday was probably when I was about seventeen years old when I went to Jersey with my friend. We flew from Inverness to Glasgow and then got the 'plane to Jersey.

We were expected to provide our own entertainment and this was mostly outside on the farm. My two sisters and brother were all close in age and we would play together. We had pet lambs and they would run up behind and bite us.

We had collie puppies who sat on the back of our bikes. They would jump off and as they did the change in weight and their manoeuvres would push us off our bikes. All good fun!

As teenagers our regular haunts included the Young Farmers Clubs. These were located all round Inverness and the surrounding areas. I went regularly to the Nairn Young Farmers Club. The Friday night dances were held in the village halls. There were also special dances held three or four times a year which were held in different hotels. On these occasions everyone dressed up - girls in long dresses – fabulous dresses; the lads in kilts or bow tie and dinner suit and that was the way we lived up until three or four years after we were married.

Anne: I was born in 1940 in Crieff, but due to my father's work we moved around quite a lot. In 1945 I lived in Brechin and was sent to the local primary school. One day I came home swearing like a trouper and there and then my father decided I would be sent to private school. I was picked up in a Lagonda car every day and taken two miles to school – very posh.

Mum bought groceries from a van that came to the house. Dad kept bees and I remember my mother would trade a section of honey which was on the comb in little wooden squares for goodies from the van, often small treats for us.

We ate a lot of pheasant and game. Father was often given them as pressies. We ate very well. I am sure folk in the town didn't eat so well as there wouldn't have been as much available; we were very privileged. We would come home from school to a pan full of fried potato. Next we would have high tea which would be a main course e.g. meat and tatties, eggs, bread and butter, jam and **one** cake – we were not allowed two cakes! We used to get half a Penguin biscuit - yes only half because they were so big then! We definitely didn't have pasta. On one occasion after the war we went to a posh relative for tea. I was told to be on my best behaviour. When we got there we were given macaroni and cheese which we had never had before and we didn't know what it was. On the way home my mum said how disappointed she was. She had expected something grander. Of course, there were no stir fry meals or ready meals at that time.

In 1951 we moved to Dumfries. I recall when I was about eleven years old we were in Carlisle and went into House of Fraser because we had heard they had Crunchie Bars. My mum, my sister and I waited for what seemed like hours in a queue that weaved in and around the shop to buy two Crunchies. Mum was so excited. I guess it took a long time for stuff to come back into the shops after the war.

In 1954, at the age of fourteen in we moved to Inverness and lived at Dochgarroch. I always remember my friend Lynne saying one day, "Don't have school lunch, come to my house. My mum has got bananas." I had never seen a banana and so I was excited to see what it was like. When we got there Lynne's mum had poured lemon jelly over the sliced banana. I was so disappointed and couldn't eat it. In fact I still don't eat bananas to this day.

When I was fifteen years old our very handsome GP, Doctor Oliver, came to the house and my mother asked him to have a word with me. She was concerned because I was having a bath every day. John, on the other hand, had a bath every Sunday night, ready for school the next day!

The first holiday I remember was when I was about twelve years old. We went to Montrose and stayed in the Park Hotel. I felt like the 'bees knees'. I thought I was 'Archie'. Later, I went on other holidays, usually with my aunt or granny. I seemed to stay away from home a long time. I think my mum wanted rid of me. Ha ha! Granny had no car so we walked everywhere.

Sometimes we would walk to the next farm and sit down at an old wooden table and get some milk – straight from the cow. It was warm and frothy – it was horrible.

I was given a bike. My sister, who was six years older than me never had a bike; but then immediately after the war things were scarce and not so readily available. The era changed between my sister growing and growing older. I got lovely gifts such as a 'walkie-talkie' doll. In 1947 I was given a doll's house. My dad made all the furniture - dressing tables, beds, little stools. My mum made all the curtains out of my old dresses and the bed linen was made out of lint. I was so thrilled. What patience they must have had to make all these things. I have the house even to this day. My daughter played with it. In fact after I was married and living on Bogbain Farm in Inverness we made a conservatory to go onto the doll's house like the one on our own house. After my granddaughter was born we would get it out when she came to stay. Nowadays it is in the attic.

I went to the High School in Inverness mainly to do Commercial (which is shorthand), typing and book keeping and the High School catered for that. I hated the school because it was so big and I was used to a small country school. It was awful. When I went to tell my French teacher I was leaving to become a hairdresser all she said was, "Well Anne, you will have to be a bit more talkative" - what a laugh - I wonder what she would say if she saw me today? I got an apprenticeship at Leslie's Salon in town. I was the first apprentice in hairdressing to be paid. Up until then apprentices worked to learn the trade for nothing.

I was sweet fifteen and a bit when I met John. I first saw him at the Halloween Dance held at the Dores Hall and we started courting when I was sixteen. John would drive through from Nairn to Dochgarroch, pick me up and we would go to the dance. Occasionally a dance would be held through in Forres, so he would drive through to me, back to Forres and then back to Inverness to drop me off and then home to Nairn again. Sometimes he would keep the car window open to keep himself awake! We courted for six years and married in 1962 at Ness Bank Church and had our reception at the Drumossie.

John and I would go to the pictures and then into the Station Hotel for a drink – famous for its cocktails - that was our hide away place. We also would go to the Carlton to eat. Carlton Restaurant was THE place to eat. It was run by Mr and Mrs Craig and their three daughters. John loved the mixed grill, steak, bacon etc.. I had omelette. He would go to the Carlton on Hogmanay before First Footing. I did not get to go! But life was so much fun. I feel we had more fun than young people have today.

When I was working in the hairdressers, which was located in the High Street, I would come down the stair and just there was Cooper's the grocers and then Irene Adair's dress shop, – the equivalent today would be a shop like New Look. I would say to my father, "Dad I don't have anything to wear to the dance on Friday, I need a new dress", and he would turn round and say "Oh go on then you'd better get one." Mum would be furious.

I remember when I said to my boss I was leaving to get married he said that if I was prepared to come back after I was married he would double my wages. I was furious that he would only raise my salary once I got married – I was still doing the same job. I left the shop and went to the phone box, called John and asked him what I should do. He said, "Well if you take the offer you could have a fridge and other things you would like for the house." But I was so cross I decided not to accept!

John: We moved into **Bogbain farm** in 1962 and stayed there for twenty-nine years. It was a cattle and sheep farm. We then retired from the farm and I worked for the Blood Transfusion Service for five years. In 1992 we moved out to Kirkhill where we have lived ever since. We have a very full life. We both love golf and we play as often as the weather permits.

Anne: I am involved in the Parish Guild and I help run a coffee morning every Tuesday in Wardlaw Church in the village. I also love working with flowers and I am on the church rota for the flower arrangements. We both play bowls in Kirkhill. I curled for twenty-nine years starting in 1973. It was very social thing at first, and over time we got more involved, playing all over Scotland. We would go together to weekend competitions with other couples. John was not as keen a player as me!

In 1990, my children told me I should get a job. So I took over the catering at McRae & Dick and was so happy even though I had no experience of such things. I was there two weeks when I was asked to do a buffet for 250 people! I loved it and ended up working there for thirteen years.

When we go south on holiday we have a lovely time, but it is also good to come home to quiet roads and peaceful surroundings – hooray for the Highlands!

13. Cath Fraser

I was born in Daviot, five miles south of Inverness in 1934. My father was a farmer. I lived 2.5 miles from the school. I walked to school every day, apart from when it was very stormy; then my father would come and collect me.

My early memories of the farm were the six Clydesdale horses that we had and two regular plough-men whom we employed and who lived in the cottages on the farm. We also had a bachelor young man who helped do various jobs. My father loved sheep and he liked to look after them. We had two moorland fields on which the sheep grazed and he would walk round and check the sheep daily.

Ninety per cent of the time he wore a kilt. It wasn't a tartan but rather it was brown with a cream check. If he was dipping or shearing the sheep he wore a boiler suit. When he dressed to go to the cattle market in Inverness he wore plus fours. He was a very handsome man and he was very cheery.

As a child I was not well and at the age of eight I had a burst appendix and was in hospital for six weeks. It needs to be remembered that this was before we had penicillin. I was quite a lonely child at times because my siblings were much older than me so I had to amuse myself.

The 1930s was a time when people were very poor. Folk don't know poverty like it was then. We were fortunate not to be extremely poor because we produced our own food so we were probably fairly well off compared to most. I didn't have many toys and during the war you couldn't buy toys. However, I remember a ploughman's daughter who was a year older than me came with this new toy and I went to my dad and I said, "Margaret has a new toy. I would like one," and he said, "Margaret's dad gets his wages from me every Saturday. And see that cow Lizzie who died last week? Well it will take me weeks to make up for that loss. I have no money for toys," and I accepted that.

The school had two rooms with about thirty pupils. We had an influx of evacuees but after only one week they were gone because it was totally unsuitable due to lack of room. School was strict but I loved learning. On the walk to school I would go over my verbs and recite my poetry. I got most of my homework done on the way to school! I liked learning.
I passed the bursary to go to the Academy but I wanted to do shorthand and typing so I chose to go to the High School known then as 'The Techy'. I was allowed to choose and my father said that was fine. I was cycling by then so I rode 2.5 miles to the bus stop, got the bus and then walked from the bus stop to school. I left my bike at the Post Office beside the bus stop.

I found it quite overwhelming when I started. It was so big in comparison to the small village school. There were thirty-six in the class - thirty girls and six boys. I made friends although there were very few country girls in the class. I was only there for three years because my father took a massive heart attack and it was during the lambing season so I had to leave and help with the lambing. In addition to that we were in the middle of moving farms. I was heartbroken to leave the farm because although it wasn't pretty it was where I was born. It was the only home I had known. We were moving about fifteen miles and I had the job of painting the implements we didn't want to take ready for the sale at the farm we were leaving. Then I had to cycle two miles to the telephone to call the hospital to find out how my daddy was. It was a horrendous time. He was in hospital for five months and when he came home he came to the new farm. The new farm was at Inverfarigaig which was up what we called 'the corkscrew'. I had a step mother and she was terrified of that and she would ask me if I would walk with her. It wasn't tarmac so the road was very rough. It was extremely pretty up there. My father stayed there five years and then bought Milton of Leys farm. When I visit there now I don't recognise it, I have no idea where the farm house was – it has changed so much.

The sister nearest me in age was eight years older and was a teacher working in Petty. She had digs in Inverness. I worked in a solicitor's office in Union Street. During the week I stayed in digs with my sister and I would go home at weekends which I always enjoyed.

From a very early age I had intended not to marry a farmer. I had had enough. Being a farmer's daughter was one thing but not a farmer's wife. Funnily enough most of my boyfriends were farmer's sons. Anyway this particular farmer, who I didn't like particularly much, invited me to a Young Farmers' Ball and I wanted to go, so I went with this guy, but I met Hugh there. He was very much a farmer. His father had died when he was nine and by this time he was twenty-one so he was very much the farmer. His farm, Borlum, was out at Scaniport. It is on a very beautiful site overlooking the River Ness and Caledonian Canal. It is very isolated at night, and on a winter's night you can't see a peep of light anywhere. It was remote and very dark - no street lights anywhere.

We courted for four years because I didn't want to marry a farmer! Friday night was our special night and we generally went dancing to all the country halls such as Drumnadrochit, and Smithton - we both loved dancing. On our first date he pulled up outside the house my sister and I were staying in Ardconnel Street. I went out and he took me to this car and I said, "It's new?" and he said, "Yes and I got it especially for you." It was a Morris Oxford.

We eventually got married in 1957 in the church we were attending in Chapel Street. I remember my dad and I sitting together on our own, waiting for the taxi, and he turned and said to me, "I don't know about you but I am ready for a dram." I said, "What a good idea" and so I had a stiff whisky and I was glad I did! We had our reception in the Columba Hotel down by the river. Hugh thought he had safely hidden the car and a taxi came and collected us and when we saw the car it was awful. It was covered in pink Windowlene and there was Bostik all over the windows which didn't wash off. He spent three quarters of the next day cleaning the car. Our first night we spent at Invermoriston and then we went to Balmacarra which overlooks the Isle of Skye and then we went over to Skye.

When we returned from our honeymoon the farm house was being re-roofed and so we lived in the Bothy - one up one down but when it was time to move into the house I didn't want to. I was so happy there, but of course we did and we shared the house with Hugh's mother who was on her own. We split it in half - we had the top half and then after a few years we took over the whole house. It was a lovely place to bring up the family.

I said to Hugh I would never work outside and I never did and Hugh said, "That's good. It's fine with me. I won't do anything inside." – but he did really. My mother-in-law went into town every Tuesday and Friday. We got electricity in 1955 but we had no fridge, or washing machine, so she had to go to Inverness to get fresh meat and various groceries. We had a dairy in the house basement which had a stone floor, and marble shelves all round. It was really cold, as cold as a fridge really. So when she was in town I would go down to the farm and collect the eggs! I didn't cook when I was at home. I did the baking but that was it. So I had to learn to cook after I was married. I said to Hugh, "I can't marry you because I can't cook" and he replied, "You're an intelligent woman I'll buy you a book – a recipe book!" I had to wash the clothes by hand because there were very few mod cons.

When I look round now the big changes for me are the shops. I think the biggest shop used to be Woolies. In general the shops were privately owned and there were Italian café's where you would get coffee, and ice cream shops were all over the place. I remember going on day trips to places like Aberdeen to the bigger shops like C&A, which was great!

I love the peace in the Inverness area. Whenever I go away either to my son down in Surrey or when I have been on holiday I enjoy myself but I was, and still am, always happy to come home. When I would get off the train I would feel like crying because I was glad to be home.

14. Anne McCreadie

I was born in Lancashire surrounded by cotton mills and coal mines just after the outbreak of war in October 1939. We escaped the bombing but during the night we could hear the planes heading for Liverpool and Manchester.

Living in back-to-back houses in cobbled streets we didn't have gardens but a back yard with outside toilet and no bathroom. This meant when we had a bath it was in a tin tub in front of the fire. Blackout blinds covered all the windows and there was no street lighting (gas lamps at the time) so the enemy wouldn't be able to locate built up areas so easily.

As children we played in the air raid shelters. However if the siren went off everyone had to congregate there until the all clear was sounded. The factories round and about were camouflaged by having the rooves covered with grass.

My father born in 1901 was the eldest of seven children born into a relatively poor family. At age twelve he went to school in the morning and worked in a factory during the afternoon; at fourteen he left school to work down the pits working there until the early '40s when he became Miner's Agent – a union job.

As the mines were nationalised in the mid-1940s he got a job as Industrial Relations Director for the National Coal Board. With his job came a company car and a telephone which was unusual at that time. Most extended families lived close to each other and so they would keep in touch by running messages back and fore. If they lived further away telegrams were the most common form of communication.

I started school age four and I can still recall the name of my first teacher Mrs Gregory. Our classroom seemed quite big and had an open fire with a big fireguard. I remember grey, cinder looking balls being used rather than coal, which was called coke. Today the class would be known as the nursery and in the afternoon we had to have a sleep on small fold up beds. At playtime we were given a small bottle of milk to help build up our bones. In winter there were times when the milk was frozen. Once a week we were give a spoonful of cod liver oil followed by a little orange juice to wash it down.

At the end of the war we moved to a house with a bathroom which was very close to the school and I was able to go home at lunch time. I enjoyed my time in primary school and did well academically managing to pass the eleven plus when I was only ten years old. However, when I went to the all-girls grammar school some of my class mates were as much as three years older. I was much more immature and later realised I would have been better to have been kept back a year in primary school like one of my best friends. The excitement of grammar school was having my first school uniform with war time rationing children in primary school were not expected to wear uniform. Ration books played a big part in my early years and it was great when rationing ceased especially when you could go to the toffee shop. I often think rationing was a good thing as nothing was wasted. For example, our local greengrocer would come round every Friday night on his horse drawn cart and collect vegetable peelings which he would then feed to his pigs on his farm. Old clothes went to the rag and bone man in exchange for donkey stones which were used to whiten door steps.

There were no after school activities but I joined the brownies and later the girl guides. I also attended the church youth club where, as young teenagers, we played team games with bean bags and in summer went a nearby field to play rounders.

On leaving school at almost seventeen I went to work in the wages office at the National Coal Board. I enjoyed work and as we did the wages for several collieries there was a fairly big staff. The highlight of the week was getting cash from the bank and making up pay packets and then going to the colliery to 'pay out'. There was no such thing as bank transfer then.

I married in 1959 at the age of twenty and we had a short honeymoon at Butlins Metropole Hotel in Blackpool. I continued working at the National Coal Board until I became pregnant at twenty-one with my first child. It was unusual for women to carry on working when they had children as they were expected to become full time housewives

As a family we came to the north of Scotland in the '60s and spent time as wardens at Carbisdale Castle Youth Hostel where my youngest son was born. This was my fourth child. It was lovely in summer but so cold and lonely in winter when the hostel was closed. Today the hostels have central heating and all mod cons and are open all year round: not the case during my time!

We decided to move to Inverness. It had been expensive at Carbisdale with only a mobile grocery van, no shops nearby and we didn't have transport. So we moved into a new maisonette at Capel Insh, off Grant Street. It was lovely with a nice view of the harbour, a grassy area with swings at the front. However in the nearby side street some of the properties were reminiscent of the early '30s. There seemed to be such a lot of people living in some of them and they looked so dull and dingy. The area seemed quite derelict yet many of the properties were well maintained and spotless. The people in them were really friendly and helpful.

There was a variety of shops on Grant Street, the local chemist always there to give advice - no need to go to the doctor, just ask Charlie Forbes! Sadly I find Grant Street quite depressing now. Apart from one or two shops the rest of the properties, particularly the Welfare Hall and the old Lochiel Arms need a good facelift. There are metal shutters on all the windows in the evening when once you could walk along browsing in the shop windows.

Soon after arriving here I went to St Mark's Church on Easter Sunday. Having been confirmed in the Church of England I assumed I could take communion anywhere. However on leaving the service I was asked if I was a member of that church. It was explained to me that in order to take communion in future I would have to become a member.

I felt quite lost at first, however, one of my neighbours took me along to a Young Wives Group at St Mark's Church hall which I really enjoyed and I was a member for several years. Through attending the group I began attending a Mother and Toddler Group at the East Church Hall every Tuesday morning and it was here I met Dell McClurg and we have been loyal friends ever since serving together as key players in Merkinch Community Centre and on the Community Council. This group led to me becoming involved in the Scottish Pre-school Playgroup Association and from there I set up a toddler group in the Mission Hall Madras Street. It was well attended and I became involved and joined the steering group for what was to become Merkinch Community Centre.

Our Centre - Merkinch Community Centre - opened its doors on 6th December 1976 with a Christmas Party for pre-school children. I was soon involved in organising fund raising events, ceilidhs, Burns Supers etc. and I loved it. By this time I was a single parent and had to go out to work full time. So I got a job working with Scottish Co-op initially in the wages office. It wasn't easy as there were no benefits or child care like there is now for working parents. Quite often I had to go to work and leave my children to their own devices - anyone doing that today would be reported to Social Services - yet I had no choice.

After twenty four years with the Co-op I retired and realised that in spite of all the time I spent in the Centre there was no actual activity for **me** and so we employed a development officer to develop activities for 50⁺. This has proved to be a good investment and many new activities and changes have been made. As a Centre we had to change direction since ever younger people were going out to work or college and didn't have time to volunteer.

Things are changing in Merkinch with many new comers to the area. However, overall locals are very friendly and supportive of each other. When my youngest son died at the age of twenty-four I was overwhelmed with kindness and concern by the local people of Merkinch.

This community spirit has been very important to me and that is why I am still involved in Merkinch Community Centre after forty years, enjoying the challenge of moving with the times. After my first year in Inverness I had no desire to return down south. Apart from visiting family I know this is where I should be. I feel that this is my spiritual home.

15. Angy MacDiarmid

I was born on the Island of Lewis in 1940 and lived in Benbecula for the first eight years of my life. My father was a minister there but in 1948 we came to the mainland to a small village outside Keith called Newmill where I went to school and grew up. I was fortunate we lived in a manse; even on the islands we didn't have the hardship of an outside toilet or no running water. I remember the manse being cold. There was a kitchen and a scullery. A scullery was like the utility rooms we have today. There was also stairs going up to the maid's room where people came to stay and help my mother at the communion season.

As a child I loved sports. I played netball and hockey but was also very much into tennis. In fact I was a member of the tennis club which I attended on a Saturday. I would walk there in the morning; walk home for lunch, back for the afternoon and then home in the evening for tea. There was no café where you could go for lunch so you had to go home. I used to get the children's newspaper every week. There weren't a great number of comics available and even when I was over on Lewis for the summer my father would send it to me.

I started school at the age of five in Benbecula and continued primary school in Keith before moving to Keith Grammar School at the age of eleven where I stayed until I was eighteen. I failed my Higher English which meant I couldn't get into Teacher Training College. So I sat the Civil Service exam, passed it and was given a posting to London. However, my mother said I couldn't go to London. Sadly, my father died and my mother wanted to move nearer her family, who were still living on the islands, so we moved to Inverness in 1960 and my mother started a Bed and Breakfast and I helped with that when I was not at work.

When I was growing up we had our main meal at lunch time and then had a high tea in the evening. My mother insisted I had breakfast, usually porridge. Being of West Coast parents we ate a lot of fish which in the main was boiled. Quite often we would have salt herring, boiled meat, and stew. We also ate sausages and bacon – that was a must, but we never ate mince.

We would get black and white pudding from the islands. As my father was the minister, we were very fortunate because the local farmers would pop in a chicken in passing which was a real luxury. We didn't have turkey at Christmas - we had chicken. Family on the islands would post a chicken just with a label on it not properly wrapped - it would come just as it was. Rabbit was another thing we had. We always had potatoes, carrot, turnip, and beans but nothing like sliced green beans or sweet corn - none of the modern vegetables that we have today or indeed fish fingers or pasta.

We had desserts such as steam puddings, and trifle when visitors came or at Christmas. No cheesecake, crème-fraiche, yoghurts or ice cream. The only way we got ice cream, which was a huge treat, was when we were living in Newmill. There was an ice cream shop over in Keith and the man who owned it had one of those little carts and he used to come over to Newmill in the summer and we would get an ice cream then. Fruit was a luxury. There wasn't a fruit bowl sitting on the side for you to help yourself. Rationing was still in place and sweets were a delicacy. Because sugar was rationed my mother would say we could either have sugar in our tea or she would make toffee with the sugar allowance.

Baking such as scones, pancakes, oatcakes, shortbread and sponge cakes were done in every home. I never saw tray bakes when growing up, this was one of the 'new' things my generation introduced.

We went on holiday every year back to my grandfather's home in Lewis. We never went abroad, always back to the Island which I am proud of and that is where I still feel my heart is. There is something special about it – there is something that draws you back. Even when I grew older I had developed a great love for the island and I would still go over for the summer even after my father died.

We sat as a family - mother, father and the three of us in the kitchen at night. We would do our homework, then the evening finished with family worship and then we all went to bed at the same time. There was no television, in fact I only got a television after I was married, but we had a radio through in the lounge and we were allowed to go through, sit round and listen to Children's Hour. There was a Raeburn in the kitchen and my mother would take our clothes and warm them in front of it in the mornings ready for us when we got out of bed because it was so cold and there was no central heating.

On arrival in Inverness I applied to the County Council and got a job with no bother in the Rates Department. There were huge journals recording the name of every person and it was all divided up with various columns – one for sewage, one for water etc. and a final total column. When I went for my interview these journals were opened in front of me and my interview consisted of adding up every column and making sure it balanced with the final column. There were no calculators so you had to add the figures in all the columns in your head - that is why I don't need a calculator today, I can still add up really well in my head. The Rates Notices had to be written by hand for the whole of Inverness-shire. Once written, my boss and I would go through each one proof reading against the valuation roll. They would then be posted out. When the new building was opened over in Glenurquhart Road our department was the first to move in. I remember we weren't allowed to wear stiletto heel shoes in case they marked the flooring! You wouldn't dare call your boss by their first name and you would 'dress for work'. This meant wearing a skirt and jumper or blouse - no trousers of any kind!

I came to Inverness, which in my eyes was a great big metropolis, from a small place where everyone knew everyone and I didn't know anyone. I went to work and everyone seemed to have their own friends and they were all going out and I felt very much on my own. One day a girl said "So when are you having your house warming?" I said "I don't know who to invite." She replied "You have the party, I will bring the folk." My mother had to go over to Lewis to be with my sister when she had her baby. So while she was away my brother and I were left on our own and I had the party and that was where I met my husband Ian.

We courted for two years. When courting we used to go to the pictures which was probably the most popular thing to do. There was a lovely picture house called the Palace in Huntly Street where the Premier Inn is today. There were other pictures houses in town but I used to live on that side of the river so that is where we went. We use to go on walks, or attend dances in the Caledonian Hotel. There was none of this going out for meals or going to the pub. In our generation women didn't go into pubs, different from my daughter's generation, they are quite used to it with university and all that.

On a Saturday morning my mother would send me over to Burnett's to get fresh bread and I would meet up with Ian. He would take me to Burnett's Tea Room on Academy Street. It was a lovely place, beautiful table cloths and cake stands - a proper tea room! Across the road from there was a delicatessen and next door was Burnett's Bakery shop.

I remember the Empire Theatre which is where the Ramada Hotel is on Academy Street today. It was really good because I had never been to the theatre until I came to Inverness and on a Friday night they had a midnight matinee with stars such as Callum Kennedy, Sidney Devine and Robert Wilson - I thought the world of Robert Wilson! We would go on a Friday night to any of the Scottish acts.

We were married in 1962 in the Queen Street Church which is now the Chisholm Funeral Parlour. Our first home was a flat in Reay Street where we lived for three years.

In 1964 our daughter was born. She wasn't due until the August but I had to leave work in the April because my boss thought I shouldn't be in the public area because I was pregnant. She said "You will now sit round the corner Angy at that desk." I wasn't allowed to go to the counter to speak to any customers.

I returned to work when my daughter was a year old. In those days there was no paid maternity leave or prospects for your job to be kept open for your return after the baby was born. I really didn't have much of a choice then, but there weren't really many official child minders or nurseries in those days. Fortunately I found a child-minder who looked after her.

In my early days in Inverness there wasn't a hospice, there was Raigmore Hospital and RNI. I remember before Raigmore was renovated, I went for my antenatal appointment. The gynaecologist came in and there was only a curtain between me and the next patient, you heard everything. There was no privacy whatsoever. It was quite funny because clinic day at Raigmore was a Friday and just before nine o'clock in the morning you would go along to get the bus from the Station Hotel in Academy Street and you would see all these bumps leaning against the wall - all these women waiting for the bus!

I remember the very first set of traffic lights I saw was when we moved to Inverness. As I recall there was one set down near the Town House where Oliver's the baker used to be.

We moved to Dundee in 1965 with Ian's job and we lived there for five years before returning to Inverness. Dundee had a wonderful shopping centre with C&A, Marks and Spencer and British Home Stores (BHS). When I came back to Inverness and there was no shopping centre my sister-in-law and I would go on the train through to Aberdeen for a day's shopping, in particular to buy the school uniforms from Marks and Spencer.

Inverness used to have loads of beautiful individual shops. I recall there was a lovely book shop called Melvin's. There was also John Menzies the newsagent. There were clothes shops, pram shops and I remember a beautiful drapers shop on the corner of Inglis Street and the High Street, where Hotter's is now. It was called John Forbes. You didn't need to go out of town to retail parks and such for things. There was none of this big shop that we do now and then loading everything into the car. I would go down town practically every day to do my shopping and browse round the shops and bringing stuff home as we needed it, because, bear in mind, there weren't fridges around and there certainly weren't any freezers. I bought vegetables fresh. They would be on display in big bags and I would take out what I wanted. There wasn't much coffee on the go at that point it was mostly tea - loose tea and you would buy by the ounce according to what you wanted and could afford. There was sliced bread but mostly we sliced it ourselves. I remember Skinners the Baker at the bottom of Stephen's Brae where Girvan's tearoom is now. That was the first baker's shop to introduce fresh cream. There would be a huge queue on a Saturday waiting to buy a fresh cream cake. It was a luxury; you just didn't get that anywhere else at that time.

For me the biggest change in Inverness is the lack of individual town centre shops. For example, where do ladies of a special age group go to buy an outfit for a special occasion? Recently I ended up all the way out at Brodie Countryfare which is miles away from Inverness!

We didn't go in for hire purchase or anything like that. When we got married we knew we had the flat so we chose our furniture down in Hay's furniture shop at the bottom of Church Street. We went in, picked a two seater couch, two chairs and a dining room suite. I got paid on the 15th of the month and Ian got paid at the end of the month. So when we got paid we would go in and pay something toward the furniture to ensure that by the time we were married everything was paid for and we could take it home. We wouldn't have dreamt of having hire-purchase.

I remember buying the pram was a big adventure. My pram would be useless today because young mums want prams they can fold up and put in the car. Mine was big with big wheels, but I thought it was wonderful. I would walk into town with it, get my shopping, meet friends in the street and have a chat. Entertaining was mostly done in your own home. You didn't meet elsewhere for coffee the way we do now, you tended to go to each other's home for a cup of tea and chat.

There was a Cameron's draper shop on the High Street and one in Church Street, which is now McEwen's of Perth. The shop in Church Street sold corsets and things like that - for the older woman! The shop in the High Street was beautiful. It sold china, items for the home and had women's clothes. I got my first sheepskin jacket from there and I still have it.

It seems to me that we are now living in a throw away culture. People don't want to buy things to last. That is so different from the way things were for us, when we bought items it was for quality, and was bought to last.

Inverness is a beautiful place with so much and an exciting place to live.

16. Marie McLeod

I was born at home in Birmingham in 1940. My mother had a nurse in the bedroom to attend the birth. My granny was also there waiting to hear my first cry. I was born but there was no cry. The nurse told my mother I was still-born. My granny ran to the kitchen and returned with a pan of hot water and a basin with cold water. She took me and plunged me from the hot to cold water until I cried! My mother was thrilled and the nurse amazed!

As the war was on, my granny wanted my mother, brother and I to move back home to her cottage in Stornoway, which we did. My father had a Gent's barber shop in Birmingham but he had to go off to war. He was a sailor on a destroyer so he was in Icelandic waters for most of the war. We travelled up from England on the train and then on to Mallaig and across on the ferry to Lewis.

I started school in the village of Sandwick, Isle of Lewis at the age of four. My brother was already in school because he was eighteen months older than me. I cried every day when he went off to school because I wanted to go, so in the end the teacher agreed to let me go with him and be there. The teachers were very nice and knew that my father and grandfather were away at war. My mother drove ambulances during this time. We lived just round the corner from the school. My grandfather had a paint and wallpaper shop in the town and my mum, brother and I lived in two rooms in the shop. So I walked to school every day. I was very shy as a child but I was happy at school. Teachers were very nice and they encouraged me. I then had to move into the junior classes which were in another school in the town. By then we had moved house and we used to walk through the woods or go on our bikes to school. It was very dark in the winter as there were no street lights.

I know we didn't have such nice teachers in the primary. I remember one teacher would throw the whole blackboard at times or the board duster if we were noisy, and of course he also used the belt which had three prongs. Teachers were a bit harsh with that.

In 1950 we got a council house. It was a new Swedish house. I still remember my mother being so happy with the house as it had a proper inside toilet and a bath, lots of cupboards and a garden! Prior to that, it had been a tin bath in front of the fire, no electricity – only Tilly lamps and candles. An electric light was a treat for us all.

As a little girl I enjoyed skipping, cycling and getting to know birds and sheep and we had wild rabbits as pets. I also had a pet hen called Jemima and a collie dog called Bob. We played with cardboard toys such as 'cut out' animals in magazines and had a wee farm, the odd ball and we used to draw and sketch. We didn't have much, we just amused ourselves.

My family would hire a Shieling for a weekend - out in the country. It was out on the moor in the middle of nowhere and all it had was a bed, Tilly lamp, and a well somewhere nearby. It was freedom. It was good. We would eat outside when the midges weren't around and we just enjoyed those holiday times together.

We only had one neighbour. He was the Gillie of the River Creed and he looked after it and would allow us to fish on it.

We would wrap our neighbour's daughter in the hay without him knowing and he would put her and the hay on his back!

In 1951, my grandparents took my brother and me to London for the Festival of Britain. It was a big adventure for us. While I was there I tasted mushrooms for the first time. My granny scooped them away in case we got something from eating them! My mother was very ill and was in hospital but medical staff did not know what was wrong with her and so she was sent home and I looked after her and neighbours helped when I was in school.

At this time, I moved onto secondary school. We wore a uniform which was a navy skirt, ankle socks, black shoes and blouse and yellow and blue striped tie. We were not well off so when we got holes in our shoes, we couldn't just go and buy another pair, we had to push cardboard into the shoe to stop the water getting onto our feet. I was a Highland dancer as a child and again, if necessary, I would put cardboard into my dancing pumps. I remember my auntie and mother taking me to get my first pair of shoes that had been bought specifically for me and that was when I was sixteen.

My mother passed away at the age of forty-three. I was still in school working towards my qualifications and was also responsible for looking after the home.

I left school and my father wanted me to stay at home and look after the family. However, I applied for a job in the Civil Service but they took a long time to get in touch, so I got a job in Inverness with Frank Sime the Timber Merchant and worked in his Queensgate office. Part of my job was to measure the railway carriages and the timber to make sure the train could carry the stock to Beauly by train. Working in Inverness meant obviously I had to stay in digs. The room wasn't bad but I was always hungry, I only got cereal and a sandwich at teatime. It was terrible. However, a friend of my father was working in the Palace Hotel and she got me a maid's room in the hotel and I stayed there for a while.

When I finally received a letter from the Civil Service offering me a job with the National Assistance Board in Stornoway, I accepted and went home. This is now known as the Department of Work and Pensions! My wages were £4.7/6^d and I had to give my step mother the £4 and I got to keep the rest. I couldn't even buy stockings for that which I needed for work! I worked there for two years and then got married.

I loved Inverness. I loved the scenery around the river and the castle and the people were so friendly and kind. The old bridge with its arches was lovely but not much good for the increasing volume of traffic.

The RAF set up a camp on the island in the village of Uig. The young men used to be taken to town once a week to the YMCA where the young men and girls would meet and enjoy dancing.

I was dared to ask a young airman for a 'Ladies' Choice' dance and I accepted the dare. The young man I chose asked if he could walk me home after the dance and I said he could as long as he took my friend home too. I said, "My friend and I came together and we go home together!" We didn't see each other every day or anything like that. It was usually at the dance or sometimes he would come home to our house. When he did, my father always put on his jacket. He never greeted him in just his shirt sleeves. The young airman and I ended up getting married in 1959. My friend also ended up marrying an airman!

We got married in Glasgow. I was nineteen. We had the wedding reception in the City Bakeries. My father didn't attend but he sent me a telegram wishing us well. We spent our honeymoon in Stornoway. My grandparents let us borrow their baby Austin car and house for a week. We decided to go for a drive at two o'clock in the morning and we got stopped by the police who said we shouldn't be out at that time in the morning so in the end we slept in the car. We then went off with him to Germany and Cyprus. My first daughter was born in Cologne in Germany and my second daughter in Lincoln. While in Cyprus I worked for the RAF Police which was really interesting.

Eventually I returned to Inverness late 1969 and got a job working with Scottish Catering which was based in the dungeons of Ness Castle. In 1974 I started working for the Police as a civilian assistant. I did the court work and it was varied. I was happy to do whatever came my way and I worked there until 1991 when I retired. I have kept busy with all sorts of interests. I enjoy painting and for some time I attended the Muir of Ord art class, which I loved. People were so friendly and very supportive. I also have my little dog called Sonny who is very special and great company for me.

I love the people, scenery, the easiness of being able to get around; in fact I love everything about Inverness.

17. Drina Burnett

I was born in 1942, in Johnstone hospital near Gourock. At the time I was born, my father was refurbishing the original Queen Mary ship as a troop ship for war time. When I was about a year old, my father went off to do his stint in the war and my mother and I went to stay with his family in Edinburgh. We stayed there until I was seven years old when we moved to Inverness.

My mother was originally from Inverness and so it seemed right to return here. The family business had collapsed which meant my father could move away and start a new life. So, post war, we moved permanently to Inverness and lived with my granny at 90 Telford Road. I went to the Merkinch School starting in Primary 3.

We got milk in school and I would go home for lunch because I only lived along the road. In fact I used to go home at play-time too. I would take a friend with me and my granny would have pancakes or hot scones ready for us, and then I would toddle back. We had a lot of freedom then and we didn't need to get permission, we just went. At the age of eleven I took the qualifying exam and those who wanted to follow an academic career usually went to the Academy. Those who wanted to do Commercial would go to the High School which is what I wanted. We didn't have an enforced uniform but there was some form of uniform. At a young age my granny taught me to knit and so by the time I started the High School I was a very accomplished knitter and as a result I knitted a pale grey twin set and made green and yellow bands, which were the school colours round the wrists and bottom of it and wore a nice tweed skirt. It was quite something!

111

I remember my grandmother travelled to Edinburgh with the Blood Transfusion Service (BTS) to be presented to the Queen Mother for the work she had done with the Red Cross. She used to go to all the outlying places with a doctor to take blood.

In my granny's house the bathroom was under the stairs and she had a wash-house out the back. The Radio Times was the toilet roll - I used to cut it up. She also had gas lamps.

In time my family moved from Telford Road to St Ninian Drive in Dalneigh and my father was what was known as a Key Worker. As a result we qualified for one of the new Swedish Houses. A Key Worker was someone who was considered essential to building up post war Britain. So my granny, two of her sons - the eldest and youngest, my parents, my younger sister and I stayed there for a couple of years and then, when I was around nine or ten, we moved to Fairfield Road and my mum, granny and her eldest son moved to Perceval Road. Her youngest son got married and moved into the next street so we were all near each other and we stayed there until I left school.

In the family house in Edinburgh we lived in a mill house with its own mill in the grounds. Play for me was making things and I played in the field at the back of the house. I would play 'houses' making mince out of dock leaves - I loved playing make believe!

I seemed to spend a lot of time at my grandmother's in Telford Road, Inverness and she would take me to lots of places. She used to go, twice a week, to Fraser's Auction Rooms. We would take a sandwich and a flask of tea, spend the day there and enjoy the local Auctioneer, Wullie Michie, as he was 'entertainment on two legs'! I used to go to the sale room with my granny and buy a lot of stuff. She also enjoyed going to auctions held in large country houses. Sometimes we would take the bus to Forres, Lossiemouth, or visit the Oakwood Restaurant on the outskirts of Elgin and later walk into the town. We would have a trip to Dingwall on the bus, or travel to Fort Augustus.

I baked a lot. In fact, while I was still in primary school, my mum had an evening job starting at 5:30pm as a telephonist and my father worked till 6:00pm or 7:00pm so there were times when I was left in charge of my sister. When that happened I would bake pink buns! I listened to the radio and I loved classical music back then. I remember a Primary 7 outing to the Empire Theatre to watch the Scottish National Orchestra and that gave me a love for classical music. I remember being totally mesmerised. I went to piano lessons too but didn't enjoy dancing. However, one thing is for sure I was never bored. I had a desk in my bedroom and all my homework was ordered, organised, very methodical and my learning process was down to a fine art. I 'swotted' a lot, writing down how many minutes to spend on each area of study. I used to read 'The Girl Comic' from beginning to end. It was full of instructions on how to make things.

Each summer after we had moved to Inverness, we would go back to Edinburgh to visit family during the Trades fortnight. Sometimes we went on the bus, other times we went on the train. We always had picnics. We would get the ferry and go over to the Black Isle. We would build a fire and spend the day there.

When I lived with my granny at Telford Road, I remember going down to the Co-op. It had a wooden floor with all the sacks of food – tea, butter, sugar, biscuits everything loose and when bought, they would be packed in brown bags. On the way we would pop in and see my granny's cousin and she had a jar of pan drops and I would always get a handful.

I remember Burnett's the bakers in Academy Street where M&Co is now. The baker's was on the ground floor and the tea room was up above. I used to have to go and get the pies on a Saturday morning – there was always a queue because they were so good.

I remember the rationing - especially for the sweeties. At the top of Telford Road there was a wooden hut called Bella Man's Sweetie Shop and I remember going in there for my sweeties. In Lochalsh Road there was Johnny's, another sweet shop, and also there was Beattie's where you could get great rhubarb rock. I had a great choice of sweets! I remember too when I lived in Telford Road the horse and cart would come to the door with the coal and the groceries. A gypsy came to granny's door on occasion with darning wool and all that kind of stuff.

Round the corner from Grant Street there was a small Post Office but also at that entrance there was a passageway to a lady who was a seamstress and she made all my clothes. My granny was a great knitter and she would go out to Holm Mills and buy the tweed to make my skirts and coats and she would get some wool to make Fair Isle jumpers and berets to match. I didn't like going to see this lady for fittings because she always pushed me about, sticking pins in, and I couldn't understand why I had to wait for the clothes. In Bridge Street my granny's cousin had a men's outfitter shop called Johnstone's, which then moved to where Leslie's Hairdressers is now, opposite

Marks and Spencer, and his brother had a shoe shop also called Johnstone in Grant Street. Around the age of fourteen I got a job in the outfitters which I enjoyed.

As a teenager of thirteen or fourteen I would walk from Fairfield Road, play tennis in Bellfield Park and then go to the Ness Café where Riva is now, or The Rendezvous, which is now Rocpool, or up to the 'Soda Fountain' in Queensgate for a great milk shake.

I remember celebrations being held for the Coronation in the fields where Dalneigh School is now and I also remember the prefabs all along the canal.

We always had a roast on Sunday, left overs Monday, mince on Tuesday, Wednesday was stew day, Thursday was pot luck which meant sometimes it was soup and pudding and Friday it was fish. Saturday was different because my two uncles and my father would meet up and go to the Tenerife Lounge in the Caley Hotel every Saturday night. The three women would get together at my mums house for a 'chin wag'. She would have spent all day Saturday baking in preparation for the evening. The men would come back 'plastered' fall out over football or politics and then all go home again. Saturday meals were all built around what was happening.

When I finished school at seventeen, I went to work at Craig Dunain hospital for six months. It was a rude awakening. It was all locked wards and secure units as use of medication at that time was very limited. I then went off to Edinburgh to train as a nurse. I really wanted to do hotel management but in those days my parents were quite an influence on me and my father said that hotel management was a man's job, not a career for a girl. My granny was still alive at this point. She had been high up in the Red Cross and involved in the Blood Transfusion Service and did a lot of charity work. She was also involved in the Liberal Association of the Gaelic Society. She also influenced me quite a lot throughout my life. So when I was told I couldn't do hotel management I decided to do nursing. My grandmother was delighted.

I travelled down on the train to Edinburgh for my interview. The journey took six hours. My relations picked me up and took me to the hospital. I sat an entrance exam and then came home and waited to find out if I was successful and had a place on the course. I was indeed successful and I trained for three years at the Edinburgh Royal Infirmary. A further year was spent at the Sick Children's Hospital, still in Edinburgh, to specialise in working with sick children. While training to be a nurse you were expected to live in the Nurses' Home which was quite restrictive. For example you couldn't be out after 9:30 each evening and you were only allowed one late pass once a month. Of course this led to people jumping in and out of windows and all sorts of nonsense! The Night Sister not only went round checking on the patients but would come over to the Nurses' Home and check we were all in our rooms. I think the rules were the same in Inverness Hospital at that time too. In fact where Eden Court is situated that used to be the Nurses Home. The training was very different from what it is now. For example, my first three months were spent in what was known as a pre-training school. Then having passed my prelim I was assigned to a ward and over the three years I spent a certain amount of time on different wards which broadened my experience. While on the wards you were considered very junior and were expected to carry out duties such as emptying bed pans, cleaning tops of lockers and such like. Very basic. Our uniform was light blue and I had to wear a cap. When I went to the Sick Children Hospital the uniform was much grander. It was pink and the cap was a piece of square material which had a 'flutey' bit where the material was gathered together and held by pins. The headdress part went down the back of my head. I had to make up my cap at the beginning of every week. The collar of my dress was detachable and had to be starched. I had to wear black stockings, a pink belt, black shoes and a watch pin. My uniform was laundered by the hospital every week and I was expected to wear a clean apron every day. Nurses were not allowed to leave the hospital in uniform unless accompanying district nurses to homes or clinics. When I would go off duty I was expected to remove my apron and put on a black belted coat and hat.

Once I qualified, I returned to Inverness and wanted to do private nursing. I used to read 'The Lady' magazine every week. That is where adverts for private nursing and nannies would be placed. I was fascinated by all the different situations that were on offer and really fancied the idea of going abroad, but, once again, my parents didn't approve. I applied for some situations and people were interested in me but my family didn't approve. However I saw an advert in The Courier, a managing director of a machine tool company in London was looking for someone who would assist in bringing up his small son as well as combining some duties in the business. I thought this sounded great and so I applied. I went down to Cheam, Surrey for the interview and got the job. This time I travelled by plane. At that time Inverness Airport was out at Dalcross and was literally a wooden hut! There was no direct flight from Inverness to London so I went from Inverness to Abbotsinch near Glasgow and then from there to Heathrow, London on a VC 10. I was met at the airport and chauffeur driven to the house and stayed there for six and a half years. I lived in the family home, looked after the child and got very involved in the business. It was quite a different life.

In February 1969 I returned to Inverness. I was only home a few weeks when a neighbour told my mother that she had a BT engineer staying with her, who had noticed me and wanted to ask me out. This was repeated to me and I said, "Oh! Are you supposed to be asking me on his behalf?" I answered the message, "Tell him if he wants to ask me out, he has to come and ask me himself." So that night he came to the back door and asked me out. He told me he was going back to Stonehaven for the weekend to see his parents but would be back and would bring his car - a Jaguar. I said, "That will be right." Anyway, true to his word, he came round with his Jaguar and we went out the rest of the week and on the Friday he proposed. By the Saturday I had a ring on my finger which is still there today, forty-four years later! On our first date we went in the car to Loch Ness to a hotel near Drumnadrochit for a drink. It was cold and there was snow on the ground. In the lounge of the hotel there was a roaring fire and a grand piano. Kenny sat down and played it and that was it. The rest is history.

I went back to work at Craig Dunain when I was twenty-seven and worked there for six months. It was completely different. In ten years the style of nursing had changed and there were only two locked wards.

We got married in the October 1969 in the Queen Street Church, our family church, which is now Chisholm the Undertakers. I attended church and Sunday School there and, in due time when our children arrived we had them christened there even though by that time we were not living in Inverness. Our reception was held in the old Drumossie Hotel which was on the same site as the current hotel. We had a wonderful time and then left and stayed at the Clansman

Hotel near Loch Ness for our wedding night. The next day we set off to Edinburgh for a week's honeymoon.

We lived in Stonehaven for ten years and bought our first house, a newly built bungalow, which cost £5,000. We had central heating off the Baxi fire; you had to feed the fire to get the radiators heated.

We received some money as wedding presents and we bought our cases, an oak table, chairs, a bed, and two carpets - one for the sitting room and one for the bedroom. We had a second-hand three piece suite and when you sat on it all the sawdust came out of it! A neighbour offered me a display cabinet which we used for china and crystal. We had a 'G-Plan' coffee table and two chandeliers which I still have today. Material that I had bought in London all those years ago was made into curtains.

I recall the first year we were married I had an account with the grocer's and the bill came to £13 and my budget was £10 a month for food shopping so I had to contact my mum and ask for a 'sub'. You paid the grocer monthly. I remember shopping in the first supermarket; I left the children outside, did the shopping and by the time I got home the shopping was delivered.

We moved in just before Christmas 1969 and after that Kenny worked in the Western Isles. He would get extra money because he was away from home and he would save his money and subsistence. We went down to Leslie's the furniture shop in Stonehaven and bought a headboard, dressing table, chest of drawers and two bedside cabinets. And I still have them! We didn't buy anything until we had the money.

Kenny's wage was £84 a month and my salary was £48 a month and we bought a house on that! I had started a part time job nursing at Cornhill Hospital in Aberdeen. Travelling back and forth to the hospital was difficult and Kenny was working away quite a lot. As a consequence I had a miscarriage and Kenny said that travelling and working in Aberdeen was too much. I then moved to a job in Woodcot Hospital in Stonehaven. However, shortly after that I fell pregnant again quite quickly and had to leave. I gave birth to my son Glyn in 1971 and my daughter Roz in 1972. I returned to work doing night duty and Kenny's parents looked after the children. When Glyn was two he was diagnosed with diabetes and the following year Roz was diagnosed with a blood disorder. Following these two incidents, Kenny was offered promotion and he said he would take the job on the understanding that I would stay at home with the children. I agreed and we moved to Elgin and lived there for the next twenty-three years.

Kenny retired at the age of fifty-seven but was doing contract work until he reached sixty. As a result he stayed with his mother in Stonehaven during the week and came home at weekends. She began showing signs of dementia and was living on her own by this time. On one occasion she was not well and Kenny called me saying Social Services wanted to admit her to Cornhill Hospital Aberdeen. What should he do? I said, "Throw some of her things in a case, put her in the car, lock the house and bring her here to me." That's what happened and I cared for her for five years. At this time my own mother also was showing signs of dementia and I was travelling up and down in our wee red mini to Inverness three days a week, while also caring for my mother-in-law. I said to Kenny we should look to move closer to Inverness. That move happened because my uncle, who lived in the house we live in today, died. My aunt who was also living here decided to go into a nursing home. When my uncle died he left various items to different family members and I was left the grandfather clock. We came to see the clock. On the way home that day I said to Kenny, "I hope one day we will never regret not buying that house." He was not convinced but a while later we were back in the house and Kenny said, "If you really want the house we can put in an offer and see what happens," which is what we did and after some discussion our offer was accepted. We moved in along with the mother-in-law. This enabled me to look after her and my parents.

18. Evelyn Sinclair

I was born in 1942 in a small village in Dunbartonshire. I was born at home in a fairly big house. The house was a 'tied house' with my father's job at MacGruer's boat yard.

Due to my father's job, we moved when I was four to Sandbank in Argyll. For some reason I had already started school in the village so when we moved, I went to the new school. Again we had a tied house. I remember it was an old traditional stone built Scottish building, two storeys, and in its own grounds. It had been divided and an elderly couple lived independently upstairs with their own entrance and we had the downstairs rooms. It did have a bathroom and we had a range in the kitchen but I remember my dad and uncle removing the range and putting in a coal fire. I also remember we would sit up in the sink getting washed at night.

As a family of six we sat in the kitchen round the table and ate our meals. I must have been about four when my brothers and I were allowed away from the table one evening while my mum and dad had their cup of tea. I remember coming back with knitting needles and a ball of wool - poke poke – "Show me how to knit mum, show me how to knit." I said, and she did. She also taught me to sew. As far as toys were concerned I don't remember having many. The main toy was a golliwog.

Years later, when her life was coming to an end, my mother had sorted the house and there was a bag of wool all sorted into small balls in the craft cupboard with bundles of fabric. I found a small piece of material about three inches high and it had been stitched into a kilt with a small gold safety pin as the kilt pin. It had been something I had made as a small child. I remember thinking, "My mother has kept it all these years - that is amazing!"

We were bussed to the secondary school in Dunoon which was about four miles away. If we missed the bus we had to walk, and as time went by we biked. I got my first bike when I passed my 'quali' - which was the qualifying exam for secondary school. It was quite traditional at that time for children to get a bike for passing that exam.

Where we lived in the village meant we were the last to be dropped off. The bus would then go to the terminus and turn round ready for the return journey so we didn't have very long for lunch. We had a large garden and the bus driver could see us running down the hill and round the corner. He was good enough to wait for us.

Because I started school quite young I was one of the youngest in the class but I was promoted to the higher class. When you were in primary school the teacher had two classes in the one classroom, and so if you were doing well you could be moved to the other class. I was Dux equal of the primary school.

I attended Dunoon Grammar School and placed in the academic stream. We studied Latin and French and for the first few years we also studied sewing but not cookery. When we got to fourth year my needlework teacher wanted me to do my Higher exam in needlework but my parents disagreed. They wouldn't have understood much about further and higher education from their own background. I think the view in the village was that if you were a girl and bright, then you would be a teacher and my parents had that in mind for me so there was no way I would be doing a Higher in needlework as far as they were concerned!

From the age of four, my father's married sister, who had only one daughter of her own took me on holiday with them each year until I was seventeen. In the early days I would go to her home. In later years we used to go caravanning all over Scotland.

An important memory for me was the Cowal Games in Dunoon. Attending them each year was a true tradition. We would walk or go on the bus down to the pier and wait for the pipe bands, who would come off the boat, march through the town playing and we would march along behind them. At the end of the day there would be fireworks. It was always a wonderful occasion.

I had a university interview at sixteen but was rejected because of my age so I went at seventeen. I was still interested in sewing and at the age of sixteen I saw an advertisement in the newspaper for a factory seamstress at the Edinburgh Woollen Mills in Dumbarton. It really caught my eye - it just jumped at me, so I asked my parents if I could apply for the job. They gave me permission never thinking it would come to anything. I stayed with some relatives who lived in Dumbarton, went for the interview, got offered the job, and accepted it. I returned home in the afternoon and caught the school bus back to the village. Everyone wanted to know where I had been, so I organised for everyone to take various text books back to school for me because as far as I was concerned I was leaving. I had it all organised but of course when I got home my father put a stop to that and I didn't leave school until I went to Glasgow University for three years. I left there with an MA in Geography and Modern Studies.

I lived in the university hostel which was specifically for girls who lived out of town. I then went on to Jordanhill Teacher Training College but also carried on at Glasgow University doing the first part of the M.Ed. degree. I completed the diploma and at the end of the first year I met my husband who was from Nigeria. That was in 1963. While at university I took driving lessons. Learning to drive following the trams in Glasgow was no easy feat but I did pass my test.

We got married in 1964 and went to Nigeria. I found it fascinating. It was very different. One observation I noticed whilst we were in Glasgow was if we were out walking together we would naturally hold hands and be close. However, we would often get abuse being black and white together. When we went to Nigeria our holding hands totally disappeared because it was not allowed in the culture.

My husband was the first Nigerian manager at the biggest power station in Eastern Nigeria. Prior to that, there had always been an ex-pat manager. As a result the Nigerian Government sent my husband to the UK with a view to him qualifying and returning to that post. For me my lifestyle was significantly improved when I arrived in Nigeria. I had employed house girls and cooks, gardeners and drivers. My husband was very wise and he chose to bring a couple of girls and a boy from the local village situation. This gave them the opportunity to improve themselves and their skills while I lived the life of luxury.

We lived in Nigeria for four years. My husband found me a job teaching at a boys' mission school - the Church Mission Society School. I drove ten miles to school each day on a small scooter that I had. I was considered a very valued member of staff in their eyes because I taught English in English because I was a British person. I taught French because it was part of my degree. I also taught Geography because that had been my main degree subject and to top the lot I taught Colonial History which was very interesting! I was the first non-Nigerian teacher and the only woman teacher. It was a wonderful experience to teach students who were keen to learn. I would go into the classroom and they would stand up and I would say, "Good morning boys." They respond by saying, "Good morning Madam."

The civil war broke out in 1967 and began to get serious. Massacres started happening around the country. It got very difficult and I remember sitting outside on the upstairs veranda half asleep when I heard this low droning sound. It sounded like a lorry driving up the hill near the house and I was vaguely waiting for it to change gear. I suddenly realised it was droning on for a long time and when I looked up I saw a plane. I sat watching not thinking and then I saw something drop out of the plane and realised we were being bombed! I got the girls and we went down into a shelter that we had.

We fled from there and eventually ended up at my husband's village where we stayed. Life suddenly changed dramatically for me and when faced with such situations you realise material possessions become meaningless. We moved into a small mud hut, our room was 8'x10'. We were privileged because we had a bed. Others lived on floor mats. We cooked outside - an outdoor kitchen. Being married to the eldest son I had my own kitchen with a wood fire like a camping fire. The children brought the water from the local river – there was no running water. For showering there were cubicles in the courtyard of the village built from palm fronds where you went with your bucket of water. A wrap would be slung over the top so everyone knew you were there and they would come and peek in to see if I was white all over!!

At first I was a trophy - I was white, university educated, I could knit and sew – these were trade skills from which people made a living. However, after four years and I wasn't pregnant I fell off all these pedestals. I was considered a barren woman which was seen as a major disappointment and that was a tough time for me.

In 1968 we left the village and moved to the northern part of the province where my husband had a new job at the aluminium mines. We had a bungalow to live in and I was pregnant by this time. You could still hear the bombing and shelling coming closer and food was very scarce. Sometimes there was nothing to eat. I wasn't very well. The tradition was to feed up pregnant women so they would give me what they had. One time the workmen brought some dried meat, something I hadn't seen in a long time. I was very grateful for it. They asked if I enjoyed it and told me it was snake meat, then between them they were laughing and saying it was human meat – I will never know!

My daughter Brenda was born in June 1968 and by September if we hadn't agreed we would come home she wouldn't have survived. She was three months old when we left. I was only allowed to bring her out because she was a female child. It was a scary journey home.

We went to my parents initially. I had nothing and I was five stone in weight. I tried to think out what to do with a small child, and so I decided to go back and finish my M.Ed degree. On my return I stayed with the Polish couple I had previously lived with as a student. I had been married from their house so they were delighted to have me back. I got funding as a mature student and finished my studying and went back to teaching.

Fortunately there were nursery places for my daughter, which helped me.

When my daughter was three years old, my husband asked us to come back to Nigeria as the war was over. However, the folk in my local church were very supportive and they challenged me that if I came up with £500 they would sponsor me for a mortgage to get my own flat. Although I was working as a Researcher for Social Work in Glasgow at the time I had no way of finding £500.This information went back to my husband and he gave £500 to one of the Catholic missions in Biafra and the nuns in this country gave me the money. So I bought a flat where we stayed for three years. I remember furnishing it and making it home and I never got into debt.

We did return to Nigeria but it was absolutely horrendous. There were soldiers with guns everywhere and wherever we went I would be stopped, searched and questioned about why was I, a white person in the country just when war was over? Brenda was three years old and she would say to me, "Mummy where are the soldiers taking you? Are they going to shoot us?"

Everything had changed and there was so much turmoil. In the end I realised I couldn't stay. So I put some of my wages away until I had enough and one day I took Brenda and left. I never left a note; I just left returning once again to Glasgow with no luggage just my sewing machine.

We stayed in various places I worked, Brenda went to school and then years later when I was living in England, I came up to Livingston to a wedding. While up there I went along to the church of the friend with whom I was staying in Edinburgh and met Ron in 1980. We started corresponding and eventually got together and married in 1985.

I had a knitting machine and I was putting Celtic designs into my work. These designs came from my time on Iona with the Iona Community. Ron was intrigued by this and encouraged me to develop the work further. Ron wanted to move to Inverness to be close to his brother and so we moved into Muir of Ord and we set up business there. Because the Council realised we were employing people and bringing work into the area they gave us a Council house where we stayed for nine years.

Ross-shire Council came up with a fantastic offer of £10,000 for anyone who would vacate a Council house and move into private accommodation. So we applied for that, found a house in Inverness only to find the offer withdrawn for various reasons. However, we eventually secured a mortgage and bought our house where we still live to this day.

I love living in Inverness. I particularly love the Islands and the fact that there is a clean river running through town. I also love the fact that you can live in a city and yet be so close to the country, beautiful scenery and so many places to visit.

19. Chrissie Cumming

I was born in the very centre of Glasgow on the banks of the River Clyde in 1945. Six of us lived in a single end tenement with a room and kitchen and on the stair heid there was the cludgy.

My first memory was us flitting from that house to a brand new scheme in Priest Hill which was just outside Glasgow on the south-side in Renfrewshire. My father, sisters and uncles went off in the flitting van with all the furniture and I went with my mum and aunt on the bus and it was pitch black. I remember my mother and aunts with what looked like turbans round their heads and they were filthy.

I remember when I was about six years old one Hogmanay my parents took all six of us to the pictures and we walked along the Clyde and saw the lights and the rabbits. Afterwards we went to the theatre and they bought us a poke of chips and we caught the last bus home. We didn't have very much money but they made it a special time - It was magical!

I started school when I was five and I went to about six different primary schools because they were building schools for the over spill from Glasgow at that time. I remember this very old school which was like Central School and there were fifty of us in one class.

Then I moved to Priest Hill School which was much smaller and I stayed there until I was seven when we moved to the Highlands. I attended Central School which I didn't like because I thought the children were very cruel teasing us about our accents. As a result I kept my mouth shut, but having said that every year I won the Burn's Prize for reciting Tam O'Shanter.

We were known as teuchters in the street because my father was a Highlander and he spoke the Gaelic. My father was a good man and gave us the best of everything he had.

We moved to Laurel Avenue into a three bedroom house almost the same as the one we had left. The person who had lived in the house worked for the railway and he had obviously got some paint from work and painted the house dark green and dark brown and my mother just burst into tears when she walked in. The furniture was sent up by Pickford and the flit cost £100. It arrived two days after we arrived which meant we had to sleep on the floor. It was just like camping out!

I didn't play many games when I was a child. When we were in Glasgow there were a lot of street concerts and I used to sing in them. From the age of nine I worked the sewing machine for my mother because it was an electric machine which was too fast for her. She took in repairs and sewing for folk and I had to help her with that. Then when I was about eleven years old, my mother got a job and I became the house keeper. I did all the cooking, cleaning, washing and ironing for six of a family which meant I didn't have time for playing games.

My father kept saying "education is easy to carry" and so we had to stick in at school. As a child I had had to wear callipers and I remember in one class I wrote a story about wanting to be a nurse so I could pay back to the nursing profession for the help they had given me. I won a prize and from then on everyone assumed I wanted to be a nurse.

I also remember my teacher in the sewing class telling me off. We had been told to cut out a doll's outfit and so I did and I thought I was then supposed to sew it up, and I wandered over to the sewing machine and started doing that. The teacher turned round and said, "Girl you come over here, don't you dare start working on that sewing machine." I said "I have been on a sewing machine since I was eleven years old." She was not amused and told me not to cheek her back!

I left school on the Friday and started as an auxiliary nurse at Craig Dunain Mental Hospital on the Monday. In July 1963 I started training as a mental nurse which lasted three years. When I qualified I became a Registered Mental Nurse (R.M.N). My father didn't think mental nurses were proper nurses and so in November 1966 I was seconded by Craig Dunain Hospital and I went to the R.N.I hospital to do my training to become a Registered General Nurse (RGN). I got paid £12 a month. I had to give my mother £6 because I was living at home. When I was in the RNI my father went to see the matron and told her he expected me to be allowed to go to midnight mass even when I was working. The Matron sent me in my uniform, cap and all to the Cathedral for mass! I was mortified.

Our first training sessions were carried out at the RNI where Eden Court is now. Unlike Craig Dunain, RNI didn't feed us very well - we were starving. We used to get turnip soup. Where the grounds are now they used to grow turnips and tatties and we got fed out of that. We called ourselves Pavlov's dogs.

Miss Lowe the Matron invited me to the students Christmas Party. There wasn't any music or anything and she would go round the table and everyone was expected to stand up and do something. I was lucky because I could get up and sing. When she discovered how well I could sing she invited me to sing at every doctor and sisters' soirees. It was a real pain in my backside!

I met my husband at a local dance. He was a true Merkincher having lived in Ord Terrace and the prefabs prior to us getting married. I was only sixteen at the time and still in school. I made it very obvious I wasn't interested in getting married or anything until I had qualified and done what my father wanted me to do. He continued to be interested in me so we married in 1970 I got married the year I qualified as a general nurse when I was twenty-four.

I was still very poor in these days and so my parents were happy to provide a small reception but I had to pay for anything else. However, an amazing thing happened. I was caring for a lady on Women's Medical – Ward Nine and I was telling her that I was getting married. As it happened she worked in Hoares Bridal Wear shop at the back of Woolies and the day she was being discharged she gave me her card and told me to go and see her in the shop. So after my finals I went to see her and there was a sale on. She told me to have a look at the dresses which I did. I thought this isn't the place for me because the dresses started at £25 and that was too much money for me. Anyway she asked if there was anything I liked and how much she had appreciated me looking after her and so I picked out one that I liked – a plain but lovely dress. She took it and ripped the seams on both sides and she swept it across the floor so it was slightly soiled. She took it through the back, came back and sold it to me for £10 - I couldn't believe it and never forgot her for her kindness to me. I didn't even have to have it cleaned because the soot just brushed off!

The reception cost £64 and was held at the Loch Ness Hotel. My father was tea-total and my mother stuck the money into his pocket but forgot to mention what the money was for. Off he went and at the reception he offered all the guests a drink and so of course he paid with the money in his pocket. At the end of the reception he and my mother went to settle the bill and my mother told him the pay the money and he asked what he was to pay it with. She said, "The money I gave you!" Needless to say they explained to the manager and promised to return on the Monday and pay the bill!

My husband and I bought a flat in Carlton Terrace. We had very little furniture - I was minimalistic just didn't know it then! I loved auctions and would go to them and buy nice furniture when I could.

In 1970 when I was eight months pregnant the Matron spoke to me and asked me what I was going to do when the baby was born. She said, "You have cost me a fortune to train. I will give you work one or two nights a week, go away and think about" which I did. I had the baby on the Friday and on the Sunday Mr 'OMO' Sutherland, charge hand for Parkinson's Heating Department came to the house in his boiler suit which was very unusual. People didn't come to your house dressed like that. Anyway I thought he had come to see the baby, when he turned round and said he was making my husband redundant. Well that was it, I got up and showed him the door, phoned the hospital and said I would be in Monday night and my husband was going to be a house husband! I went back doing night shift and did what is known today as a job share with another girl called Beryl. We would work our hours between us to suit ourselves and it worked really well. Craig Dunain was a lovely hospital to work in. They treated the staff and patients very well.

We moved to Drakies in 1972 and bought a bungalow but I hated it. The people there treated me ok because I was a nurse. However, they treated my husband really badly as he was considered working class because he was a Heating Engineer.

In 1977 I had my daughter and we moved to Kenneth Street. It was a working B&B in 1977 back over this side of the river. It was in a terrible state so I went to Cameron's in Church Street, opened an account, bought everything I needed and made it beautiful. My son was football crazy! He was always dressed in an Aberdeen football strip. One evening two boys about ten years old came to the house looking for a goalie for the Grant Street League and they offered him the position which he accepted. The League got to the final and played against Hilton Street League. The game ended and the score was 7-0 for the Grant Street League. I was quite chuffed and couldn't help smiling. It was my first football match – the first of many!

I moved into the area, loved the house but the area was really run down, so I got in touch with the local councillor and went to see him with my list of twenty-seven things needing to be done. The councillor told me I didn't know what I was talking about. I pestered him for a while but didn't get very far. I decided to stand as a regional candidate which I did and at the election in 1990 I won by four hundred votes. I then had to go out and do the job I had been girnning about and I stayed on the council for twenty years. I thought I would get help to settle into the job. However, this was not to be the case. Fortunately, one day just after I was elected I bumped into a previous District Councillor in Merkinch and she said she would help me. True to her word, for the first four years she guided me and encouraged me. I always remember her with great affection. I held the position of Chair of Social Work and part of my area was Merkinch. People would write in asking for funding and I would have to check it out and decide whether we should support the request. I went to the Merkinch to see what was happening. One Tuesday night, there was Elsie Normington with her keyboard and five or six people singing along. In those days folk came along just to sing together and I thought that was great, so I sang and spent half the evening there. They were all laughing and joking. I told Anne McCreadie that I would be back. I was and have been involved with Singing for Pleasure ever since. I am so proud of being part of Singing for Pleasure. Every time I walk in the building I get a huge sense of pleasure. It is another place I call 'home' and I feel I really belong.

For approximately twelve years I was involved with the 'Soup and Run'. This was a service for vulnerable people who needed food and support. We prepared the soup and sandwiches at St Mary's Hall and then took it all along to Bank Station and the Town House every Saturday night.   I also volunteered for 'Contact the Elderly' where I would welcome people who were lonely into my home on Sunday afternoons. I could have up to sixteen people for tea those Sundays!

As I approached the end of my working life I was concerned about what I would do with myself. I needn't have worried because I feel needed and cherished and I have so many friends old and new.

I love the people, the river and the fact that it doesn't matter what religion you are you are treated just the same. I feel there is no bigotry

20. Ian and Jane Fraser

Ian: Before we start I will tell you I am a great believer in that's women's work and that is men's work! My mother taught me to cook, she never taught me to iron. My father said, "That's women's work"!!

I was born in Forfar, Angus, and completed my primary education in Dundee. We moved there when I was five and then returned to Inverness when I was twelve years old. I attended Inverness High School. My father was from Inverness and my mother was from Angus. They met during the war. My grandfather was a shepherd out at Culloden Battlefields. I used to come to Inverness for my holidays staying with my grandfather on the farm and later, after he had retired, in Castle Street. I always liked Inverness. When it was decided we would move there I was quite happy. As a twelve year old, I thought that will do me fine and even now I think there is nowhere else I would rather live. At one point I would have liked to go to Canada but that was not to be. I had the opportunity but I turned it down. Jane was close to her parents and so we stayed here. I was educated mostly in Inverness, spent my entire working life in Inverness and I am happy here.

As boys we played football - all boys played football. I would also walk for miles in the country because I was very interested in nature and loved being outside. My mother would say, "Come home when you are hungry."

Jane: I was born in Stephen's Street in Inverness in 1946 and always lived in Inverness. My father was Invernesian and my mother was from the Black Isle.

I went to Crown Primary School and then on to the High School which was known then as the Technical High School. At the school you could do what was known as commercial or domestic courses and I was allocated to do domestic and obviously English and Maths. I left school when I was fifteen.

As a youngster I loved to play with dolls and I still have my doll that was given to me many years ago by a neighbour. Dad used to go to Wembley to football and he brought home a clockwork toy soldier on a horse, and a toy 'Muffin the Mule' which had a magnetic nose. When you put a plastic carrot, which had a magnet in it in front of the mule, it would move its head. I used to spend hours with both those toys. We played outside but not far because there were always cattle coming down the Brae to the Mart. We used to stand on the Brae quite a bit and just watch what went on or go to the swings at Macewen Drive (beside the Bowling Green) where we spent many happy hours.

Birthdays were just another day apart from the orange cake my mam would bake. Even Christmas Day wasn't that different. Again dad would be working. We would get an orange or apple and a sweetie in a stocking but we didn't get big gifts, we just couldn't afford it. Again mam would make a lovely clootie dumpling for New Year. That was a wonderful treat. My mam was a great cook and baker.

In the early 1950s when I lived at home we had a tin bath in front of the range. To fill the bath with hot water would have taken a lot of bother and time so I would share the bath with my sister. It wasn't a daily routine! However, we did have an inside toilet but no toilet roll - it was newspaper on string! However, in time we welcomed the arrival of Izal toilet rolls. A big improvement!

Ian: I can remember when I was in school getting a job as a message boy in a grocer shop and I got 12/6^d a week. My mother would take the 10/- and I would get the 2/6^d to myself and think I was king – 2/6^d!

I left school at fifteen and I started my first proper job. The Youth Employment Service placed me into the Royal Hotel, which is where Clydesdale bank is now in Academy Street near the station, as a Commis Chef. In my first three months I worked sixty-six hours a week for less than £3 which was totally illegal. Even then boys fifteen years old were only allowed to work a maximum of forty hours per week. I left school one Friday and started at the hotel the following Monday morning. The very next morning, I was left on my own in the kitchen to prepare breakfast for the entire hotel as well as making scones and pancakes for afternoon tea. I wasn't trained. The most I had ever cooked was bacon and eggs for the family and here I was suddenly in the kitchen of a hotel. I will remember to my dying day there were all these 'old wifie' waitresses with their caps and pinnies wanting eggs 'sunny side up', eggs turned and I thought I have got to get this organised. So I got a tray of eggs and fried the whole lot and put them on a hot plate. By the time they got to the dining room you could have soled your boots with them. The next day, the chef came in and physically knocked me all over the kitchen, kicking my backside, and hitting me because I made such a mess of things.

The kitchen was upstairs and supplies came in at the entrance on Union Street. There were a lot of green grocers and butchers and Mr Rattary used to bring it all in. All the vegetables were fresh of course - no frozen vegetables. It was the job of the kitchen porter to prepare them.

The milk was delivered in churns. But the milk delivery man would come and leave it at the bottom of the stairs because they were all so scared of the chef! Another thing I remember is they would make up the menu in the morning which included sherry trifle for lunch. The head chef would send one of the junior boys down to the bar for six glasses of sherry and then he and the second chef would be waiting for the lad to return. On their return the two chefs would have three glasses each and hand over a bottle of sherry essence which was for the trifle! I had always wanted to be a chef, but it was absolute slave labour so I didn't stick it long.

My mother eventually took me to the Youth Employment Office and they offered me another hotel. I said "No, forget it." It was less than £3.00 a week. My first shift started at six o'clock in the morning till two o'clock. I had 2pm-5pm off and then was back in for high tea and dinners till ten or eleven o'clock at night. I was expected back the next morning at six o'clock - remember I was only fifteen years old. No employer would get away with that now. Youngsters wouldn't stand for it but we just accepted it. That was the way it was.

Sometime in 1960 I went to work in Burnett's the bakers, it was **THE** bakers back then. They had a big tea room in Academy Street where M&Co is now and they did all the baking of the cakes and fancy stuff. The bread was made along the Longman. They had a huge fleet of vehicles and their own garage, so I went to work in there. After a while I went to work for my father who had a coal merchant business and worked there a number of years. That was very hard work too. Then I got the chance of a job with a company called SPD who were the delivery agents for Unilever. They had a depot where Wickes store on the Longman is now. Our area went to Elgin, Newtonmore, Skye and Harris. I worked on the van delivering and then in the cold store for the next twenty-three years until they built the present A9. With that came supermarkets and they had their own cold stores in Bathgate and so there was no need for us and the work eventually petered out. I was the last one to go. After that I went on to Highland Industrial Supplies (HIS) and MacGregor's and finally retired. I was never without a job. I never signed on. I had no formal qualifications. Neither of us has, but we never ever signed on from leaving school till now.

Jane: I worked in Cameron's the Chemist in Greig Street for Mrs Morgan, where I worked from when I left school for the following twenty years and I loved it. After this, I worked for Murdo and Dorothy MacKay, at the Kingsmills Pharmacy. Initially I worked in Dorothy's perfumery shop where I sold brand perfumes, cosmetics, toiletries, candles, handbags and fancy goods. After it closed I moved across the road, where Boots Kingsmills is now, to the pharmacy and stayed there for seventeen years. I worked every Monday to Friday with a half day in the middle of the week. No chemist shops were open on a Sunday, but all of them had to do a duty Sunday rota for a couple of hours for urgent prescriptions – changed days. I had a duty every eight weeks or so. At that time there were loads of chemists all of them privately owned. They were lovely. Boots was the only chain as you would call it and they were in the High Street where Hotter's shoe shop is now. Even to this day, old Invernesians refer to it as Boot's corner - a great meeting place.

Ian: We met in 1963, got engaged in 1964 and married in 1965. I spotted Jane in the shop where she worked and thought, "Oh, she's alright!" So I tracked her down and went knocking on her door to see if she would go out with me.

We used to go to the Playhouse Cinema which was situated in Falcon Square round the corner from The Filling Station. It was a beautiful cinema and absolutely huge. They said they were going to re-build it but they never did. There was a café in it. Mr Nairn, the owner, used to do a scene/display for children at Christmas and there was a fish tank – it was a lovely place to go. It was open every day but Sunday.

Jane: Ian and I were at the Playhouse cinema the night before it burned down in 1972. There was a picture on that night – it was the 'Grand Prix'.

Ian: Dinner dances were very popular in the '60s and '70s. Once a year there would be staff dinner dances. These would be held at hotels in town, usually at the Station Hotel, now the Royal Highland Hotel. You would get a three course meal and then you would dance. It was very much a social event. We would go to the BT one which was held in either the Drumossie or Caley Hotel where there would be huge numbers at them.

We got married in Crown Church in 1965. In fact, Jane is actually on the Cradle Roll there and we still attend. Jane helps in the Sunday School and I sing in the choir. We had our reception at the Caledonian Hotel – the old Caley. Now it is the Mercure Hotel in Church Street. Our honeymoon was one night in The Tilt Hotel at Blair Atholl and then one night in Dundee – two nights honeymoon and then back to work the next day!

Jane: When we first got married we stayed at Ian's aunt's house in Caledonian Road for about a year. Later we bought a flat in Telford Road. It cost £1,950 and we had to put down £500 deposit for which we had to save up.

Ian: I was earning £12 a week. Originally the owners wanted £2,000 pounds for the flat and when I told my family solicitor, Mr Carlton, he said, "What? Leave them with me" and he got £50 off it! A few months later Mr Carlton came up to the house and took us out for high tea to the Carlton Restaurant which was in Inglis Street. That was a real treat for us. If it had been left to us, we would have gone to the fish and chip shop!

In the early days of our marriage I used to go to the public baths and swimming pool (over near the Friars Bridge) for a bath. As a child we used the tin bath and as the eldest I would always get the clean water!

Jane: When we were married we had a gas cooker and had to put a penny in the meter for the gas. We had our first telephone in the 1970s. Before that if you wanted to call anyone you had to go to the phone box.

The first luxury item we bought was a fridge. I used to do all the washing by hand on my half day off work. I used to go over to my mother's because she had a deep sink so it was easier to do the sheets. She also had a hand wringer. I eventually got my own spin dryer.

Jane: For holidays we were quite lucky. We did a bus tour in 1967 on the Highland buses and we did a fortnight's tour of Europe for £50. It was our first time abroad. We went down on the sleeper steam train to London. We were then picked up at the station and taken to Dover and over onto the Continent on the boat.

Ian: We were only allowed to take £50 in traveller's cheques and £15 in cash. We were really wet behind the ears. Jane had never been out of Scotland, and I had only been to Newcastle once. Other passengers on the trip were business people so they had the money and I remember one of the men saying to me "Where have you got your extra cash?" We didn't have any extra cash. They were stuffing £5.00 notes down their shoes, down socks, and the women down their bras!

The Continent was a real eye-opener! For example, pubs in Inverness closed at 9pm in those days. Whereas we arrived back from a day tour and the bus driver took me for a drink to some cafe which was open at midnight and the owner made us feel so welcome!

There have been a lot of nice buildings pulled down in Inverness. The one building that really bugs me is the Post Office in Queensgate designed by Alexander Ross, the same architect who designed the Cathedral. They pulled it down and put up one of exactly the same dimensions in glass and concrete. The original had been a beautiful building. Alexander Ross designed most of Queensgate, Union Street and Ardross Terrace. It is such a shame.

Jane: We used to walk everywhere, though Ian had a bike to get to work and he gave me a bike for Christmas one year too.

Ian: Our first car was a wee mini, registration number PWE 752. Amazing! I can recall the registration from a car I had in the early '70s and yet I couldn't tell you the registration of the car I have now.

Jane: Food was very plain. In the main we ate stew, mince, soup – nothing out of the ordinary. We had our main meal in the evening much as we do today. I basically did what my mother had done she had her own recipes for soups. I had the same ingredients but I could get a different soup! We didn't have much breakfast. We had no fridge so we shopped daily. In the summer we would put our milk and butter in a basin of cold water to keep it from going off. Jimmy Munro was the fruitier and we would buy fruit and vegetables wrapped in newspaper from him as and when we needed. Shops were open until six o'clock Monday to Saturday with them closing 'half-day' each Wednesday. When we stayed in Telford Street I would get the groceries in Grant's on the corner of Grant Street where Nicol's is now. The flour and sugar would be weighed out and put into brown bags. Cheese would be cut with a wire and wrapped in newspaper. Little hygiene in those days and it doesn't seem to have done us any harm! There were no supermarkets and even when supermarkets came along we didn't shop there, we shopped locally.

Ian: The first supermarket I remember was the Co-op in Montague Row and then Lipton's came to Bridge Street.

Inverness was a thriving place. It had big boat-making businesses with all the trades – sail makers, rope makers, all of them were there to maintain the ship building industry.

We have family who have moved away and would never return to Inverness. Inverness has changed and not necessarily for the better. It is too big now. However, we have always loved living here, and have been very content and wouldn't want to live anywhere else.

21. Isla Cuthbert, Hilary Paterson, Sheila Watson, Maureen Fraser, Elizabeth Cunningham, and Tina Foss

Hilary: I started school in 1952. I went to Central School for a couple of years until Dalneigh School was built. I used to live across the road from the school so I could get up at 8:50am, mother roaring at me, and run into school. I then went to the High School, and I still walked. I came home for lunch, had a two course lunch, and back to school. At secondary school I studied Commercial. Sometimes people teased me because I was at the High School doing Commercial, implying I was not very clever, but I did pass my eleven plus exam but I wanted to do Commercial so I went to the High School instead of the Academy.

Sheila: We also had deportment lessons where we would put books on our head and have to walk around balancing these books.

Hilary: I left at the age of fifteen. My father died the September before my birthday and I felt I had to leave school, get a job and help my mum – my four brothers had already left home. A sister of a friend of mine was looking for an office junior in her office and told me about the vacancy. I had an interview and went straight into the job. I started in a chartered accountants' office as a short-hand typist.

Sheila: I went to Central School before moving to Dalneigh after it was built, but because they didn't build enough classes we had to return to Central for a year and then back to finish at Dalneigh. I always walked to and from school, went home for lunch and I remember Foxy's in Tomnahurich Street (which is

146

still there) because I used to go there for sweeties and they used to have a halfpenny box, a penny box and a tuppenny box. After seven years in primary I went to the High School.

I left school when I was sixteen after I passed my 'O' levels, but before leaving I had a part-time job in the Maypole when I was twelve and another one down the Haugh. I also studied Commercial. When I was leaving school I was offered three jobs all full-time. I took a job in a chartered accountants' and stayed there for six months but had to leave because I was pregnant. I got pregnant at seventeen and I didn't really know what was happening to me. I was getting hate mail so I begged my mother to let me go away from Inverness but she didn't want me to. However, in the end she agreed and I went to this place run by the Salvation Army down in Dundee called Florence Hill. It was like a prison. Part of it was a private hospital where women paid to go and have their babies. For the likes of me we were used as skivvies, almost starved and treated like dirt and on Sundays there would be a service and we would be made to go up and confess 'all our sins'. We were made to eat out of tin bowls. I can remember starting labour and I didn't have a clue what was happening. I had gone to the loo and my waters had broken and I screamed out and one of the girls came in and told me what was happening. Sadly, I was sent to scrub the kitchens and when my labour was really far on I was taken to a ward but the gas and air machine was broken. I remember one of the ladies who ran the place saying to me "Well that is what you get for getting pregnant when you are not married. You deserve all the pain!"

Most of the girls there went to have their babies and then have them adopted. They were kept in a huge nursery and people who wanted to adopt would come along, look at the babies saying things like "No I don't like that one it looks too fat" and then pick one. We weren't allowed to feed the babies ourselves. My parents didn't have a 'phone so I asked one of the girls there to phone my aunt and ask her to call my dad at work and tell him I had had my daughter. My mum found out she was a granny when dad came home from work. He said, "Well I will have to get into bed with a granny tonight!" They came and picked me up and I came home. My mother didn't go out to work, so she helped me and looked after my daughter when I went back to work. You got no help and no money from the State or anything. I started working in the Co-op office and there was a flat above that became vacant which I got for 5/- a week rent and 5/- a week rates. I then got married.

I worked for the Co-op for thirty-seven years. I started off as office junior making tea and answering a 'doll's eye' switchboard, and then moved up to secretary, on to PA and then Administration Manager. Finally I was a Regional Training and Personnel Manager working all over the UK, retiring early at the age of fifty-four.

Hilary: In Montague Row we had the 'hole-in-the-wall' sweetie shop and they used to sell paper cones and penny dainty's, now a quarter of the size!

Elizabeth: I also went to Central School like the others but I didn't start there. During the war my mother left Inverness and went back to Elgin to stay with her mother while my father was away, so I went to a school in Elgin for a few months. When my father came home we came back to Inverness and I started 'real' school at Central. My parents had lived in what was known as 'Rooms' in Huntly Street. However, after the war, everyone was being re-housed. One Christmas Eve, we were re-housed into a prefab down in the Carse. From then till the summer time I had to walk from the Carse to Central School every day by myself and I was only eight years old. My folks decided it was too far and so I was moved to Merkinch School for the rest of my primary education. It was a really good school. No-one ever failed their Eleven Plus. My teacher's claim to fame was no-one ever failed their Eleven Plus and no-one did! We were too frightened to fail it. I passed the exam but I chose to go to the High School because I wanted to do Commercial.

Once the course was started you had to stick with it through to when you were fifteen. More often than not that is when the majority left to start work. I left school at fifteen and my first job was with a civil engineering company down the Longman where the new Arnold Clark showroom is now. I worked there for three years and then left and went to the Royal Bank and was there till I left to have my family. Of course in those days women left work when pregnant and that was it. If after you had had your family and you wanted to go back to work you had to re-apply. Jobs were not kept open for you. At that time mortgages were based on your husband's salary, nothing to do with the wife's earnings, so the banks knew the mortgage would be paid. Your job was at home. When the children went to school I took a part-time job so I could be home for when they came home.

Maureen: I also went to the Merkinch School and I remember in the infant department using slate and slate pencils. We would go in after lunch and put our arms on the desk, put our heads down, and have a wee sleep.

When I was six, my family went to live in Ullapool for two years. We then returned and lived in Dalneigh but I went back to Merkinch School. I walked back and forth every day on my own or sometimes with friends. I went to the Academy because my father thought I should be a teacher and I thought that was a good idea too. However, when it came to it I didn't want to leave home – which I would have had to do to study in Aberdeen. Instead I got a job in the Potato Marketing Board for three months and then I moved to the Railway Engineering Department as a Tracer. It is like a draughtsman but it was tracing the drawings done by the draughtsmen using blue oiled linen material. It was very interesting as I learned what was going on in Inverness. A lot of the railway property was being built on and all these alterations had to go on the drawings in pencil, while others were marked in ink. We had an ancient photocopier in a case that the carpentry department built. It was fiddly to use and it worked, but not very well. Once the plan was copied it would be put in a cardboard tube and filled with ammonia. I worked there for three years until I got married and had my family. In the 1970s I returned to work at the Halifax Building Society as it was back then.

Maureen: My bank didn't have a copier it had a Gestetner and carbon copiers. You could only do so many with the carbon. We had rows of filing cabinets and ledgers all very laborious.

Tina: I lived seven miles out of town. I went to Heatherley House School in Culduthel Road which was a private school. I was there for two years and I loved it. However, it closed which meant I had to move to Crown School. I was filled with horror. I remember the first day going out to the 'loos' which were wooden boxes out the back and every one of them was full and overflowing with faeces. I had to wait the whole day until I got home to go to the toilet! It was so primitive. Absolutely revolting! Teachers hit with the leather strap and I had never been hit. It was a Victorian building and you had to go up stone steps – it was like living in a horror story.

The Headmaster, Colonel Mackintosh was, from a young child's perspective, absolutely huge. He had a bright red face and would scream at you. I just wasn't used to it. I had come from this very delicate little place. However, I survived and eventually moved up to the IRA. That was alright and then at sixteen I had an argument with the Rector – known as 'Fat Lips'. I was terrible at Maths but I thought, "Well it's probably quite useful to have Maths", and I was doing alright in French but thought, "Well if I want to learn French I will go to France." So I went to see the Rector and for an hour I explained my position asking him for extra Maths and to be allowed to drop French. However, he said "No" and went on about how important Maths was and I couldn't drop it and that was it. He obviously hadn't listened to anything I had said. So I went home and the next day got my mum to go up to the school to return my books and I never went back! No-one contacted me to persuade me to return to school. So I got a job in the Trustees Savings Bank in Lombard Street. It was very primitive with hand written ledgers and so forth. The first job I had to do was stoke the boiler. I stayed there four years and then went South.

Hilary: I used to have to get the fire going in the mornings too. Your coat was on till ten o'clock by which time the place had heated up.

Maureen: I remember a Primary 7 teacher who would throw the board duster or chalk at you, or she would get her long board pointer and come round and slam it down on your desk. On two occasions the point came off. I also remember on occasions she would lift her table and just let it go and the ink would all come out when she was cross or we were being too noisy.

Elizabeth: Children in Primary 7 today wouldn't put up with the way teachers treated us then.

Tina: You are right. I remember one teacher and she would thwack you across the back of the head, practically knocking your brains out. It would be considered assault today. We also had a teacher called 'Buckie' who used to throw calligraphy pens at you and an electric fire came in my direction one time.

Hilary: I hated school. I was petrified of the place. We had 'The Beast of Belsen' for English. I remember even after I left school I would cross the road to avoid her rather than have to pass her; she terrified me.

Sheila: We had a typing teacher who rapped our fingers with a ruler, and a French teacher who threw the blackboard duster at us and of course the 'beast' for English who loved using the belt.

Isla: I didn't get abuse at school because I went to a Ladies College in Edinburgh. The worst that happened was you would be asked to stand outside the classroom. I lived on, what was then, the outskirts of Edinburgh and would travel by bus and then walk to school. I did this from the age of five until I was fifteen. When I left I went to secretarial college and from there went on to work in the Royal Bank on the secretarial side of the staff department in a nice old building in St Andrew's Square, Edinburgh. I was there for three or four years. They had a good training programme for juniors and when you completed your training they moved you on. So I was transferred to the West End branch where I was assistant to the full-time secretary of the manager. I didn't like it because I was expected to do non secretarial jobs. I left there and went to work for Heriot Watt

University in the Careers and Welfare department where I worked for ten years.

Elizabeth: I remember the Coronation in 1953. Down where we were at the prefabs we had a committee who collected money for weeks before and on the day, in a field at the end of the houses, we had a huge marquee and everybody came and we had fancy dress. I was dressed as Cyril Scaffy (newspaper cartoon character). It was a great day and as children we got to go from school to the cinema to watch the Coronation. I got a Coronation Bible and mug.

Maureen: I remember being up at the Bught Park on V.E. day. We had a bonfire and fireworks and I remember dancing round and someone let off a squib which burned my aunt's fur coat!
I also remember going to the cinema to watch a film about Edmund Hillary conquering Everest. It was announced on Coronation Day that he had achieved it.

Tina: As a child I spent hours and hours throwing a ball up against a wall, skipping all day. I played most of the day outside.

Maureen: It is really nice seeing the children out playing because I often say I only see children these days on their way back and forth to school. You never seem to see them at holiday time and they can't all be at their granny's!

Hilary: My husband would go off for the day fishing as a lad. He would take a packed lunch and it was just a matter of coming home when he was hungry.

Sheila: We would go swimming. Everyone had a card that you had to take and a penny and each time you went you got the card stamped. In our teens we spent a lot of time at Bellfield Park, and we loved roller skating on the Islands.

Sheila: Sometimes we were allowed to go up to the canal to watch the men opening up the lock gates with big poles. There was a house up there and at Easter time they had a lot of chickens and we would go and see them. I had a black china doll and I remember she broke and she was sent to London to the dolls' hospital to get fixed.

Hilary: I used to walk to town with my mum pushing my doll's pram. My granny was a seamstress and she made the covers and the likes for the pram. I also had a cot with a canopy.

Elizabeth: I didn't have many toys being born at the beginning of the war. However, my father was in the Faroe Islands and he sent home a doll. When it arrived I was desperate to play with it but my mother said I was to eat my dinner and then I could get it, but I didn't want to eat my dinner, I wanted the doll. I loved this doll. It had a soft body and a china face and I called it Sally.

Maureen: My grandfather made me a doll's cot and cradle with rockers and a desk.

Hilary: I used to play buses on the stairs and give out tickets and go and ring the doorbell when I wanted the bus to stop. I drove my mother crazy! When I was six and my niece was two her mother came to collect her one day and found me with this toddler in my dolls pram walking down Limetree Avenue. I never thought anything of it.

Maureen: That was another thing we used to do. We would go and take a neighbour's baby for a walk round the block in their pram.

Sheila: When we went shopping, we would take our children in their prams and leave them outside the shop while we got our shopping. That was the 'done' thing. However, I remember one day I went down to Laurel Avenue to get some shopping for my mum and I took my daughter in her pram. I got home and took the shopping in. Mum just assumed she was outside. Hours afterwards she asked me where my daughter was - I realised I had left her at the shop! All ended well, she was still there when I returned to get her and I got her home safely!!

Elizabeth: It was common when someone passed a pram to stop and look in to see the baby. If it was the first time you had seen the baby you would give it something silver like a sixpence. This was a sign of good luck.

Sheila: We were also in Brownies or Guides and we would go camping at weekends. I particularly remember once we went from Dalneigh to Balloch which was all fields then. We all piled on the back of a lorry which had no sides. We had to put up our own tents, meat for meals was hung in a box up a tree so the animals didn't get it and we also had to dig out our own toilet!

Sheila: On Sundays I would go to church to Bible Class and Sunday School, but I wasn't allowed to go out nor have friends round. I can remember the demonstrations when football started being played on Sundays. I also remember going on Sunday School picnics. We would go to a field out at Ardersier where we would go on the bus with our parents. There would be sports events and games. I was also in the church choir and we used to do pantomimes every Christmas.

Tina: When I was at school I didn't go out during the week. However, at weekends we had lots of fun. I used to love attending the Hops - Doc Hayes Club and that is where we would go to be with friends and meet boys.

Elizabeth: The thing was in your teens and early twenties you went to dances at the weekend at the old Caley Hotel and you went for a tea or a coffee - you didn't go for an alcoholic drink. That's what the older folk did!

Tina: I remember going to the 'Young and Old' in the Caley ballroom. It was usually around Christmas time and parents would take their children along for a dance.

Elizabeth: The Northern Meeting Rooms was a large ballroom in Inverness which held lots of grand balls as well as local dances. Many popular bands of the day appeared there such as Johnny Dankworth, Sid Phillips and Ivy Benson's 'Ladies Band' to name but a few. Every year during the 1950s and early 1960s, in September/October times, at the Northern Meeting Rooms in Church Street (which is opposite where McEwen's of Perth is) a special ball was held. Princess Margaret would attend a ball and at twelve o'clock lunch time she would appear on the balcony of the Meeting Rooms and we would go to see her.

Maureen: Yes, if a lady went to a bar by herself it was frowned upon.

Hilary: I used to go to Strathpeffer to the dances. The men in the Navy would be there – but I didn't tell my mother that was where I was!   When on a date, the boy would pay or sometimes you would go dutch.

Tina: Quite often it would be "I will meet you inside" then you would have to pay for yourself to be admitted!

Hilary: I remember that after being on a date to the cinema with my future husband, we would go to the West End chippy and get a sixpenny bag of chips.

Tina: When you came out of a dance or the cinema or where ever, if someone had a car you would jump in and go down to Burnett's bakery down the Longman and get the hot pies. All good fun!

Hilary: When I got married in 1967 I had my list of a hundred guests and they came for the lunch. At 6:00pm the wedding finished and we went off on our honeymoon. It wasn't the thing to have a separate function in the evening. We spent four days in Edinburgh and I was taken to the Zoo. That was it.

We were fortunate we were able to get a small bungalow to live in at Smithton. That was considered to be so out of town then because there was no bus service at that time. So we got a wee green Standard Eight. I think it cost about £160. We were thrilled to bits with it.

Tina: The weddings were not as lavish as they are now. I went to Irene Adair's for my dress and it cost the princely sum of £25.

Maureen: I went to Glasgow for my dress and it cost £36. I had my reception at the Drumossie Hotel on a Friday. We didn't have our wedding until 3:30pm in the afternoon and so it went on till after midnight. We went by car travelling and went as far as Shrewsbury. On the way back we stayed with my aunt in Ayr.

Elizabeth: We didn't have hen parties. The day before the wedding you would see the bride-to-be tied to a lamp post at the bottom of Academy Street, covered in flour and she would be left there until someone came and untied her. You would see the groom-to-be on the back of a lorry covered in soot and ringing a bell. It was called 'blackening'.

Hilary: I was petrified of that happening to me, so I told the folk at work I was getting married on the Saturday. For confetti the staff collected the paper out of punches for weeks before and then threw it over me.

Elizabeth: It was the custom to have what was known as a 'Show of Presents'. A couple of weeks before the wedding neighbours and friends would come round to the house and see all the presents laid out and then you would have a drink and something to eat. Everyone took an interest in a wedding!

Tina: Holidays were part of our lives. My family used to go for a month to Hopeman, forty miles away near Elgin. We used to rent a cottage there. There were lots of families from Inverness there who we would meet each year so it was good. I would be up at eight o'clock in the morning and straight out after breakfast. My parents didn't expect to see me again until 5pm when I was starving. Scary to think I was left on the beach by myself with siblings and friends.

Maureen: Usually we went to relatives one year and then they would come to us the following year. I remember the first time I went on a proper holiday it was to Aberdeen. I was twelve and we stayed in a B&B. It was great.

Elizabeth: My holidays were either at my grandparents in Elgin or Grantown. My mother was working so I would be shipped off for the seven weeks summer holidays to Elgin and then at Easter I would go to Grantown. I had thirty cousins in Elgin so we had great fun. I would be up and out playing – it was marvellous. Eventually, as I got older, I was allowed to take my bike with me. The first holiday we went on as a family was to Edinburgh when I was fifteen and I remember feeling really grown up. We were shopping in Princes Street and my mother and father wanted to go somewhere I didn't want to go. They allowed me to get the bus back to where we were staying and I thought, "Oh my, how grown up am I."

Hilary: The first holiday I remember was when I was three and we went to Butlin's Holiday Camp in Ayr. My father hired a cottage in Nairn during school term one year and so I had to travel through to school on the bus which I thought was great. It gave me the chance to do my homework!

Isla: We used to go to Skye. My mother's family came from Skye and we also took a cottage on a farm near Dunbar for a month. My father would come and join us for two weeks and after that at weekends. I would play with the children on the farm and go out with the shepherd.

Tina: Nothing was organised. We would sit talking and amusing ourselves playing 'jacks' and things like that.

Sheila: At one time my dad had four jobs at once and I remember coming home moaning asking could we go on holiday. My dad said, "I don't work for the Railway like Mr Calder up the road, I work to make sure there is food on the table and good shoes on your feet." So that was me told!

Tina: Shopping was done near enough on a daily basis and when my mother went shopping she used to get dressed and she always wore a hat.

Hilary: Mine too, and when she came home from the shops mum would always take off her nylons and change her clothes.

Isla: I had left my job in Edinburgh and trained for a year as a Careers' Officer. The Careers' Service moved from being part of the Labour Exchange to being part of Education Department. Highland Council advertised a job and I just wanted to work in a rural area so I applied. With my qualifications I was considered an 'essential incoming worker' and I got relocation money to come up here and there was a Scottish Special House waiting for me. This was 1975. At first I was very lonely because I didn't know anyone but I covered the country schools and I had to travel around Highland which I loved.

Tina: Inverness was always home but I lived down in Hampshire for thirty-six years but when my husband died it just made sense to come home to the familiar. For me the difference between here and Hampshire is the slower speed of life up here and people take the time to talk to you. In Hampshire it felt to me very cold and uncaring, whereas I notice assistants at checkouts up here will talk to you. It is lovely. There have been many changes. For example, the population has doubled and with it have come more facilities. Having said that, there is still a feeling of familiarity. Most of the old buildings are still in existence albeit their usage has changed. And one thing is for sure the mountains never change!

Sheila: I love that I have always lived here. It is a beautiful city. I love the river, the Islands and the canal all easily accessible.

Maureen: I think it is sad that the beautiful old buildings have been taken down. Yet I love the location of Inverness on the Moray Firth and the top of the Great Glen. The friendliness of its people and to know it is home!

Elizabeth: For me, I agree it is sad to see the disappearance of many beautiful buildings but I love the location and pace of life. The surrounding areas are beautiful and so easy to access.

Isla: I love the friendliness of the people. The lovely areas in the city such as down by the River Ness, views over to the Black Isle but also the easy access to so many beautiful places within a short drive (no more than half-an-hour). It is an area of which to be proud.

Hilary: Inverness has changed so much from a small market town to a city. There are many incomers now that you never meet people you know as was the norm several years ago. The town centre has changed with so many out of town developments. Nevertheless, I love Inverness, it is where I was born and I have never wanted to leave. When I do go away I feel homesick and I am glad when I return home. I feel very lucky to live here.

22. Dell McClurg

I was born in 1950 in Campsie, Lenoxtown in the same hospital as Lulu! I came to live in Beauly at sixteen months old where I was fostered out from the Stirling County Council Children's Home. I had a good home. My dad worked in the Hydro Schemes at Glen Morrison which meant he worked away for weeks at a time. My mum went on to foster more children so when we got a new baby she would go to the railway station at Beauly to collect it. As a result I thought that was where babies came from!

I attended Beauly Junior Secondary School. The Primary Classes were in two buildings and across the playground were the secondary classes. Children from the Beauly Catholic Primary School and from outlying areas also attended the school. Children who passed their Eleven Plus could choose to go on to the Inverness Royal Academy or to go to the High School. I chose to stay on at Beauly while my sister went to the High School

We often went through to Inverness on the train to visit my foster mum's married daughter who stayed in West Drive, down in Merkinch, now called Carnac Crescent. I have early memories of playing out in the back field which is now the nature reserve. There was a park with swings and a roundabout and a big slide. At the front of the house there was a square with flowers, shrubs and bushes and all around it there was an iron railing. We would swing on it and do somersaults round the bars like "gymnastics'! I remember the horses grazing on Carnac Point just behind the bus stop on Kessock Road. At home in Beauly I would play skipping, Skitchie and Cowboys and Indians. I also loved my hula-hoop and throwing a ball

162

against a wall and catching it. We spent a lot of time "down the river" - the Beauly river - fishing and paddling.

I left school at fifteen and got a job in the local Chip Shop. However after one week the children's home found out about it and did not approve because of the long late hours so they set up an interview for me at Woollies (Woolworths) in Inverness. I did not want to work there but got the job and had the stick with it. My dad said I could not leave unless I got another job to go to. At the time the shop had counters and shop assistants were allocated a counter for which they were responsible. There were all sorts of counters selling boot polish, haberdashery, childrens' toys. Upstairs there was a food hall with fresh fruit and veg, and a biscuit counter were you could buy a bags of broken biscuits. You could be called to go and cover any counter and I liked it when I was put down stairs on the sweetie counter. I worked there for six months and then went to a position in Pringles Holm Woollen Mills. I would say that almost 60% of the staff came from Merkinch. We got the "Workers Bus" from the town which was a double decker and it was always full of people setting off to work.
I made friends with the girls, some from Merkinch, and I would go to their houses after work. We would then swap dresses before going out for a night. As a result I spent a lot of time in the Merkinch area and loved it

On Friday and Saturday nights we would go to the 'Strath' (which was the Strathpeffer Pavilion) where we danced the night away to different live bands. It was great and certainly it was the place to be. Buses were put on especially to take people there. In fact there would be up to four double decker busses leaving from Inverness, stopping en route to pick people up along the way. Sometimes I would go with the girls from

Inverness other times I would jump on the bus in Beauly Square. Buses also came in from Tain and Invergordon.

When I was eighteen I left Beauly Village. I was pregnant and went down to Edinburgh to have my daughter. I chose to go to a Mother and Baby Home. My mum asked me to stay and have the baby in Raigmore but I felt I needed to get away to think about my life and what I was going to do. When my daughter was born we moved in to a bed-sit in Portobello but I felt very isolated and had no one to talk to for support.

I saved every penny possible so I could afford the train home to Beauly for a wee holiday and show off my baby, which I did. Back in Edinburgh I tried everywhere for a job but could not find one to suit nursery hours and I was struggling to make ends meet. So I phoned home and spoke to my mum and told her how things were and she said, "Your Dad was just saying he missed you and the bairn so you should just pack up and come home." Again that is just what I did. I lived at home for a few months until I got somewhere of my own. In fact I got a Caravan in Alness for a while before moving to Invergordon. Sometime later I moved to Inverness into a wee house in the Haugh. I lived there for over a year until the Council allocated me a flat in Merkinch and I have been there ever since.

I have always loved Merkinch. I remember going to visit my mum's married daughter. We went to a neighbour's house and it was full of adults. I was just a child and they were having a fish supper. They just took some of the food off their plates and put it on another one and gave it to me. I couldn't believe it. I had never seen anything like this before. I never forgot that kindness. Years later, when I came here to live, I noticed how things had changed. I couldn't believe the poverty and the state the houses were in. There were windows with no putty in them so they rattled in the wind letting cold air in. In fact ice covered the glass on the inside in winter and there was no proper heating. Basically the houses had not been properly maintained by the council. It was really bad. We would fill glass lemonade bottles and fabric conditioner bottles with hot water to take the chill off the beds. We only had one coal fire which heated one room giving us hot water when we could afford the coal. I thought this is not the way people should be left to live so I got on my 'soap box' and started fighting for things to be done to improve the houses.

There were a lot of kind people living in the area, but there were some not so nice who had drink problems. Drugs were not such a big problem then. Some of the lassies I knew from the dancing days had moved out of the area which was sad, but I soon made new friends.

For quite a few years when I first came to live in the Merkinch there were a lot of women from the area working at the Thornbush slipway gutting the fish. I remember seeing them at 10 o' clock in the morning coming down the road towards their house with their wellie boots and big plastic aprons on going home for a tea break and then back to work until lunch time. There were loads of boats in the slipway and lorries waiting to load up with fish would be lined up in Thornbush Road. In the area there was also a lot of little trades going on and Thornbush House had workshops in there with various things going on.

At weekends we would take the Ferry Boat over to North Kessock where we would have a picnic. The children would climb rocks and play in the rock pools on the shore where the Kessock Bridge is now, or we would go up Ord Hill for a walk where there are great views. If anybody went on a Sunday they had to keep an eye on the time because the last ferry boat went at six o'clock in the evening so they didn't want to miss it!

My daughter started school and went to Coronation Park School which was a prefabricated building, built after the war. It is where the Corbett Centre is now and it was a lovely school. The teachers were very good and it was a caring school. After two years she moved up to Merkinch School and I was quite shocked. Here we were in the '70s and there were outside toilets over a hundred years old and just awful. I looked around at other schools and they were being refurbished and yet Merkinch School had been forgotten - just like the houses. It wasn't that the school roll was falling or anything like that, it had just been forgotten. So when my friend Anne McCreadie asked me to join the Merkinch Community Council I said I would. I thought maybe I could help make a positive difference. I met Anne at the Mother and Toddlers group at East Church when our children were babies and we have stayed friends ever since

In the early 1980s I, along with other people living in the community, started going round the area looking at the state of the houses and fighting to get them updated and made habitable. It took five years to get the council to put money into the houses and it took another five years to complete the renovation of all the houses in South Kessock. However what we had not calculated happening was that it broke up our community. People who were friends and neighbours were streets away and some moved out of the area altogether. We all had pleasant centrally heated houses, but we had to build up our community again.

Then the Council decided to close the school. However, we got together and fought to keep the school open and we won that battle. I am the mother of five children and all of them attended Merkinch Primary School and then moved on to the High School. They have all done well for themselves and I am very proud of each of them.

Some of the biggest changes I have seen has been to the High Street. It is sad to see so many empty shops. I also think it is sad losing all the shops in Grant Street. It used to be a thriving, busy place. Everything could be bought locally from the butchers, bakers, the shoe shop, haberdashery, with goods ranging from nuts and bolts to cough medicine. There was a shop with everything for a new baby including the ordering of a pram! I love Merkinch. I can go into the town at night and not feel safe walking home until I am across the Black Bridge and into Grant Street. I guess that is because I know everybody and I know if I needed help someone would give it to me. I have been around various places in Inverness but none compares with Merkinch to me. I can sit in my house, look out of my living room window and see the Black Isle and dolphins swimming up the river. From my back bedroom window I can see dolphin coming into the harbour. Red Kites and herons fly over my house and the deer come along the shore. I have seen a deer behind the bus stop on Kessock Road! I love the nature reserve and most of all I love the people. I think you just can't beat living here.

Part Two

1. Louise Beaumont, Lesley MacIver, Lisa Stacey, Hamish Townshend (students from Millburn Academy)

Lisa: I was born in Liverpool in 1997. Four years ago my family moved to the Highlands. My parents decided they wanted to change their lifestyle - they didn't want to be in England anymore.

Initially I attended Glen Urquhart School in Drumnadrochit but then moved to Millburn Academy in Inverness about a year ago into S4. I didn't find the move from England to the Highlands a problem at all. It was all quite normal. For me the difference came when I moved from Glen Urquhart to Millburn because I had to change a lot of my subjects and Millburn is much bigger in size.

Louise: I was born in Staffordshire in 1996 and my family moved to Inverness in 2008. We moved here partly because of my dad's job and because we always wanted to live in the country. I found moving up here a good change. My mum and dad are outdoors people so this suited us well. Prior to moving to Scotland I had started secondary school, but when I moved up here I had to go back to primary school for the last year. I attended Strathdearn Primary and then the following year joined Millburn Academy.

Lesley: I was born in 1997, in Inverness and lived here for the first two years of my life. Then due to my father's job - he is in the Police - we moved to Ullapool for a few years and then to Shetland. However, about four years ago, again due to my dad's work, we moved to Aviemore.

Life in Shetland was much quieter than here. I actually lived on a small island just off Shetland called Whalsay with about 500-600 inhabitants. As a result the schools are tiny. My primary school had a total of eighty children. The high school is smaller than that because it only goes up to S4. After that students move to the main Shetland island and stay in a hostel and attend school there. When we moved to Aviemore I attended Kingussie High School and then started attending Millburn Academy about four months ago. I travel in every day on the college bus which is fine.

Hamish: I was born in Oxford in 1997 and lived there a few months before moving to Inverness. I have moved about Inverness quite a bit but always attended the same school. I went to Crown Primary and then Millburn Academy. When I was in primary school I had a uniform and it was the norm to wear it. At high school it is not so strict, as long as you have one thing such as a tie or badge that represents the school that is viewed as acceptable.

Louise: Everyone looks fairly smart because most people wear black or grey and white so it is fine.

Lisa: At lunch times we usually go in to town to the likes of Kentucky Fried Chicken (KFC).

Hamish: School does provide lunch; there is a deli bar which is good but the queue is ridiculous. Rather than wait at the deli counter it is quicker to take five minutes to get into town, queue in Morrison's or wherever, and get back to school.

Lesley: You may wait in the queue for fifteen to twenty minutes and then when you get to the counter the food you want may be gone.

Louise: When I was in the first year of secondary school in England pupils weren't allowed out of school at lunch time until the top of the school, and then only if they had a good attendance record and such. It was quite rigorous and strict. It is much nicer here.

Lisa: I think being out of school at lunch time might not be such an issue here because it is a smaller city.

Hamish: Everyone knows everyone.

Lisa: Yes, you have to be careful!

Hamish: There is a lot of sports clubs in school, and when I was further down the school I was involved in more. The tendency seems to be that the further up the school you go the less clubs you belong to.

Louise: Young people mainly hang out with their friends. I remember when I was in first year I was quite lonely and I went to the book group where we read books of authors we had never heard off, but it was good though. Occasionally we met the author after we had read the book.

Hamish: My spare time revolves around sport really. I do a lot umpiring and playing hockey and coaching. I coach the Inverness Junior Hockey Club and the Highland Hockey Youth Academy. I try and get a lot of that kind of thing done because that is where my passion lies. I want to be a P.E. teacher and that is where everything is being channelled.

Lesley: I do a lot of horse riding and have my own horses. I teach younger girls how to do horse riding. I also give a little

171

girl who has cerebral palsy a ride round and encourage her. Badenoch and Strathspey Horse Club hold their own competitions and I enter those. I have been to a few competitions on the Alvie Estate but I am hoping to reach much bigger competitions such as those held at Blair Atholl.

When I leave school I hope to go to Oatridge College in Edinburgh to study Equine Studies. I then hope to move across to Canada which is where my dad came from and then join the Mounted Police.

Louise: There isn't much to do in the local community where I live, and because I am out of town, it is not easy to get involved in things with public transport being so infrequent.

For me, when I leave school I want to do something in the care sector. I would like to train as a general nurse.

Lisa: I don't do much because I don't have much spare time. I work in the Therapy Suite in Church Street. I work Saturdays and Sundays and some evenings washing hair, covering reception, and giving manicures. I have got myself into college starting in January to do a one year hairdressing course. Once I finish the course I can get an apprenticeship which is good.

I enjoy shopping, in fact I shop every weekend when not at work! The shops I like going to include New Look and Republic. I buy things most weekends - most of my money goes on clothes and shoes.

Louise: I don't shop too much, my money from baby-sitting doesn't go that far, but when I do shop I tend to go to the likes of Primark.

Lesley: I don't do much shopping, I tend to tell my mum what I want and she gets it for me. I do shop on the internet because it is easier for me. I can order on line and have it delivered to me. I spend a lot of my money on high heel shoes. In fact I have about ten pairs of high heel shoes sitting in my room looking pretty. I don't necessarily wear them in case I ruin them. My mum has started to refuse to buy them!

Hamish: I don't do a lot of shopping. I shop when I need it, so if I was going to Rock Ness or wherever I would get the clothes I need and then wear them. When I do shop, I come into town so I can check things fit and I can also use my Scot Card which gives me 10% discount - I wouldn't get that if I shopped on line! I get my music via iTunes because it is free but I still buy CDs.

Louise: I buy CDs. My parents have big speakers in the lounge and I have to do chores so when I am doing them and they are out, I put on my CDs and turn the volume up!

Lisa: I play the music channels on the TV in my bedroom and I too turn it up and 'blast' it.

Lesley: I tend to get my music via iTunes but I will buy the CD of bands that I like. I have quite a lot of CDs of 'One Direction'.

Lisa: I have seven phones but I only use two, the others are just back-ups!

Lesley: I have two phones. I use one as a phone and the other has all my contacts so I keep it for that.

Hamish: I use social websites to communicate - after all it's free.

Louise: I have my laptop and that's me. For my nana in Stoke I will write a letter and I write to the wife of my granddad's brother every month because she likes to get a letter and it mean's something to her.

Lesley: All my extended family live abroad. The cost to call them is a ridiculous amount of money per minute so we Skype. I also use Facebook - even my grandparents have Facebook!

Hamish: Skype and Facebook are good because they are free. My uncle and his wife live in Las Vegas so it is easier to keep in touch if using Skype.

Lisa: 'Snapchat' - it is great. It won't last long but it is good. Facebook usage went down when Twitter started, but it has gone back up now.

Lisa: I always go abroad for my holiday to places such as Florida - all the hot countries and we always stay in hotels. We go every six months.

Louise: We normally go to the West Coast. We used to go camping but now we go in a caravan. Dad likes to go walking at 7 o'clock in the morning usually in the rain - well at least it feels that way!

Lesley: We go to Ethiopia usually once a year. My relations live out there so most of the time we stay with them. Having said that, we stay a few nights at Bishingari and I stayed in the same lodge that Ewan McGregor (the actor) stayed in!

Hamish: The only time I go abroad or out of the UK is on school trips such as skiing. For most of my life my family and I go camping up to Loch Morlich usually every summer and autumn.

Lesley: Young people don't really go on dates anymore. It's awkward. "Do you want to come out for a meal with me?" "No".

Lisa: That is so cheesy.

Hamish: It is a gradual thing now. You would probably be mates with somebody and then you realise you are going out as mates for ages and then you change. Nobody asks each other out.

Lesley: When you first get together with someone it starts via texts, or Facebook and it will be awkward to meet them but eventually it becomes easier. But it is not like the old days. When you do start 'going out', you don't go out for meals or that, you 'snapchat'!

Lisa: There is a kind of awkward moment when you both kind of agree without telling each other. You kind of slyly put it on Facebook or in a text and hope they slyly put it in too.

Louise: You talk to each other over Facebook. It so much more relaxed today.

Louise: A big memory for me was moving to Scotland and living in a caravan for two years while waiting for the house to be built. I remember we had two bad winters and we had no water and had to go down the road to get water from someone. We had a horrible Christmas. The oven didn't work and so mum had to boil the chicken and use a camping stove outside. It was an eventful Christmas!

Lesley: A memorable event for me would probably be the 'Up Helly Aa' festival in Shetland. It happens every year where during the year the locals build an absolutely gorgeous, beautiful Viking boat. Then at the festival everyone dresses up, people dress as Vikings and they all encircle the boat with big lighted torches. They then throw the torches on the boat and burn it. Some men spend their lives waiting to be the Leader of the Jarl Squad (that is the Viking Squad).

Hamish: For me memorable events were my caps for Scotland for hockey. Travelling to Wales, playing everything to do with the event was memorable. It was the best I had ever played as vice-captain. Usually a keeper is never mentioned so being mentioned was quite nice. Also I attended a family wedding at the Eden Project. It was one of the first weddings to be held there inside the dome. It was brilliant.

Lisa: For me one of the big changes taking place in Inverness is shops closing down. On line shopping is taking over.

Lesley: Inverness is also getting bigger. When I first lived here, prior to moving to Shetland, I lived right close to the distributor road and there was nothing on the other side of the road. Now there is housing and it is quite built up.

Hamish: I remember when they built the bridge over the road at Eastgate. I was about three or four and I remember thinking Inverness was now a massive city! I also like the fact everyone knows everyone.

Louise: I like Inverness and think it is much cleaner than other cities.

2. Alex Hilditch

I was born in Glasgow in 1997. I lived there for a couple of years before moving to Dundee which was really nice.

I started school when I was five at Longforgan Primary School near Dundee. The school was about quarter of a mile from my home and so I would either walk or cycle with my mum. Most days I would stay at school for lunch, but on occasions I would go home. My mum would meet me at the school gate and we would either walk or cycle together. The main thing I remember about being at this school was the scary head teacher.

In 2004 we moved, as a family, up to the Highlands into our house in Kirkhill. I started at Kirkhill Primary School and went into Primary 2. My home was near the school and so it was easy for me to walk there every day. Although I have never really liked school, Kirkhill Primary was a good school. There were several clubs there and when I was in P5-P7 I became involved in cross-country at lunch times.

As a child I played with cars and I had a train track and trains which were the toys I enjoyed playing with the most.

During the summer holidays we would spend our holidays in France. We would drive down to England and from there go over to the Continent on the ferry and down to the South of France. We stayed in a holiday home or we camped. Over the years we have gone to various parts of France. Those holidays have been really good. I have on several occasions attended Scripture Union camps. These were usually during the Easter or summer holidays. We would spend the time taking part in

177

various outdoor activities such as go-carting, tree climbing, high ropes and kayaking.

At the age of eleven I transferred to Charleston Academy and I am now in S5. I like some of my teachers but don't enjoy the hard work so much! I travel to school on the school bus and I have lunch at school. I have been working for my Duke of Edinburgh Bronze Award which is the main extra - curricular activity in which I am currently involved.

When I leave school I would like to work in the music business either in music production or working in a studio. If that is not possible then I would quite like to do something in photography.

I love music. I play electric and acoustic guitar and since last year I have been having guitar lessons. I also play the saxophone and have had saxophone lessons since I started secondary school. I enjoy listening to music and tend to download it rather than buy a CD.

A key memory for me was attending a concert in the Iron Works fairly recently. It was great. Actually it was a dangerous concert but really good!

Inverness has good outdoor activities to get involved in and the scenery is lovely. However, for me it seems far away from the rest of the country and I don't like the weather!

3. Alasdair MacRae

I was born in Leicester in 1996 and I lived there up until June 2003. My father is from Inverness and so we came to Inverness occasionally on holiday to see family, usually during the winter months.

I went to a Catholic school in Leicester, starting at the age of four. The school was closely linked to the Catholic Church much more than schools and churches seem to be linked up here. I had to wear a formal uniform complete with shirt and tie, which was awkward at such a young age!

We moved to Inverness because my father had been unwell and he wanted to be nearer family and have a life style change so we moved into our house in Kirkhill in 2003.

I started at Kirkhill Primary School at seven years old. I walked to school because I only lived such a short distance and initially my mum would walk with me. Normally I took a packed lunch but occasionally, if one of my parents was at home, I would go back at lunchtime. The uniform here was much more informal - joggers and polo shirt and no tie! The school was built in 1996 so it was fairly new when I started which was good as many of the local schools are fairly old. I remember it was very much 'we are all equal' and therefore I felt there was no need to push myself to excel because this was not what was expected. There were several sport based clubs such as cross-country held in the lunch time along with football, shinty and such like. I was also involved in the REAL Project which grows and sells fruit and vegetables. Being good at mental maths I was able to help with the selling. Real Education Active Lives (REAL) was set up by Inverness High School to educate those with less academic based skills about selling and the basics of starting a business. It also taught them about the growing of produce as well as outsourcing to local farmers and other such trades e.g. dairy farms.

I then transferred to Charleston Academy when I was twelve. In fact I started on my birthday. I travel on the school bus which I get from the end of my road and it takes approximately twenty minutes depending on traffic.

Again there are several clubs with a broader selection of activities across the curriculum – from Science to P.E. During my time at Charleston Academy here I have played badminton, occasionally football but I also play golf in my own time. I usually play twice a week. I am a member of the Muir of Ord Golf Club which is about six miles away. It is good because they have a strong grounding for young players or beginners.

We have family holidays where we have been abroad to places like Crete and Portugal but we also enjoy scenic holidays and, of course, we go south to England to see family and friends.

When I was growing up I had the general toys that most children play with but then I got into video games, the PlayStation and Xbox which are easier to play with friends. You could buy a game for a fiver and then play it for twenty or thirty hours whereas you could spend five pounds on a model or action figure but you get bored with that quicker. As I have got older I have been able to connect with friends through the Xbox or PlayStation and we can play games together even though we were all in our own homes.

In terms of contacting friends I will text or tweet. In fact I use Twitter more so than Facebook. The craze known as 'snapchat' is the latest thing but I think this might be a short lived craze.

I attend the St Mary's Catholic Church in Beauly and for the last eight and a half years I have been an Altar Server.

On a Saturday morning from 09:30-11:00 I help out at Kirkhill Primary School doing football coaching.

I am about to start 6th year at school. Last year I took five Highers in Maths, English, Chemistry, Physics and History and I am awaiting the results. I will be doing four Highers this year in order for me to extend the breadth of my qualifications, and enhance my chances of getting into university where I hope to study Business Management.

A big event I recall was the wedding of Prince William and Kate Middleton last year. I moaned all day because we didn't get a day off school and yet when we got to school we sat and watched it on television. I felt we should be at home watching it. I remember when I was down in Leicester, the Queen celebrating her Golden Jubilee. We had a street party and everyone at school was given a commemorative coin, which I still have. For this wedding we got nothing. Schools in Glasgow closed for the day but for some reason the Highland schools had to be open.

I think the biggest change in Inverness has to be the High Street. When we first came up here it was expanding but nowadays so many shops are empty and businesses gone. It seems bare in comparison to what it was. I quite like the fact it is safe around here but I feel Inverness is changing a lot. The weather is quite good but changes in what seems like every five minutes! However, in some ways that means you don't take the weather for granted!

4. David Thomson

I was born in Inverness in 1996. My parents lived in Skye but my mum had to come to Raigmore Hospital to have me. Two weeks later we returned to Kyleakin, which is right beside the Skye Bridge going from the mainland to Skye. I lived there for seven and a half years.

I went to Kyleakin Primary School, where the entire population of the school was forty pupils from P1-P7. There were only two classrooms so we had P1-3 in one room and P4-7 in the other and the Head Teacher was also the senior class teacher.

We moved to Inverness in 2004 and live at Milton of Leys in Inverness. At that time it was not as built up as it is now and Drakies Primary School was the school I went to. Drakies was very different to the school I had come from - just like night and day - because there was approximately four hundred children in the school, and whereas in Skye everything was taught in English and a little Gaelic, in Drakies all of the teaching was in Standard English. It was strange to start with, but because my parents are from down south it was fine and I soon adapted. I then moved to the new primary school, Inshes, for my last year in primary before transferring to Millburn Academy.

For me primary school was quite quiet. I would go to school and come home. In the first few years I would get the school bus to school but later on I skate boarded down the big hill. It was good fun but it took me about an hour and a half to get there! (Because I took some detours via Tesco etc.!)

Millburn was all right, the teachers were good craic but I didn't pay much attention – I was a bit of a rebel, I just wanted to concentrate on being a chef. I have always been interested in cooking. I watched all the various cooking programmes on TV such as Master Chef and they just inspired me to cook. Also my mum would teach me a trick or two and it all built up.

When I was at school I learnt to play the bagpipes and the guitar and I was in the Boys Brigade for eight years. At lunchtime I would skate board out the back of the school and then further up the school I would go home, get changed and go to work where I worked part time at Culloden House Hotel. They serve pretty high class food. I worked from 5:30pm-10:30pm and if there was a wedding or special function I would be in there for as long as they needed me.

I left school in 2012 and started college, but three weeks later Kingsmills Hotel approached me and offered me an apprenticeship. I worked fifty hours a week there from two o'clock to eleven o'clock and overtime would take me to midnight. I have a uniform which I have to buy but there is a Government tax relief system where if you look after your whites – wash them, repair you get money back. I have just left the Kingsmills and about to start at Rocpool Rendezvous. I went along for an interview, had a trial and now got offered a job. I can still continue my apprenticeship and my aim for the future is to be a Head Pastry Chef.

As chefs we meet up socially, and there are quite a few chefs who are also bikers so we all go riding together. So for example in August 2013, about a hundred of us travelled through Skye on our bikes.

One of the things I like about Inverness and surrounding area is the roads. I think they are pretty good and as I enjoy riding around on my bike having easy access to hit the roads and be out of town is brilliant. There are also pretty good restaurants and hotels in and around Inverness where you can get good food and as a trainee chef that is very important to me!

5. Finlay MacLeod

I was born in Cresswell Hospital in Dumfries in 1996. I lived there up until I was three and half years old. My father works as a Police Officer and so we moved with his job to Inverness and we lived in Cradlehall. We lived there for just under two years when we moved again to Skye.

Moving to Skye was a big but pleasant change because we were used to urban cities. Skye is so completely different.

When we moved to Skye, I was five and I started at Sleat Primary School which was about twenty minutes away from my home by road. A mini-bus would come to our area and pick up about ten of us and take us all to school and bring us home at the end of the day. School lunches were available but I had a packed lunch - quite healthy really - sandwich, packet of crisps, biscuit and a piece of fruit. When I think about time at school there I remember two things, a Gaelic group and an English group. I was in the English group and in P1 there were only four of us so we were in a class along with P2, P3 and P4 which still only made up to a class of about thirty.

This seemed the 'norm' to me, until we moved back to Inverness in 2005 and I went into P5 at Drakies Primary school. That was so much bigger. There were two P5 classes with around twenty-five in each.

As a youngster I played with skate boards, bikes and scooters and other outdoor activities probably as a result of living on Skye where the area lends itself more to outdoor activities.

185

The difference in moving from Sleat School in Skye to Drakies Primary in Inverness was probably similar to how I felt when I eventually left Primary and started at Millburn Academy in 2008, with the new schools being at least five times bigger in relation to the number of pupils.

I moved to Inshes to finish my primary education then onto Millburn. In Millburn we have a school uniform of black trousers, black jumpers or hoodies and polo shirts or shirt and tie. I get the bus to and from school and sometimes I have school lunch or sometimes I go into town. There is a varied choice for lunch. For example there is a pasta bar where there is a different choice of pasta every day. There is also a sandwich bar or kind of deli where you can choose your bread and fillings, and a selection of hot dishes such as lasagne or fish and chips.

When you start secondary school you are issued with what is called a Scotcard used for getting discount in shops, trains and buses. You can also put money on it and then use it to pay for school lunch as and when you need it.

There are clubs in school including a Lego club which has just started up. I am involved in football and study clubs at the moment but I am also in the basketball club.

I like the range of things to do in Inverness even if it is a rainy Sunday. I can go swimming, the cinema and for example a group of friends have hired out the Millburn hall to play basketball during the holidays. It works out about £2 each. In my free time I play football for the s.chool and a local team, basketball for the school and I enjoy playing golf.

Generally people just meet up in town or go to a party at someone's house. I also go golfing with a group of friends or some of us will go down to Inshes and play football.

I have been pretty fortunate with holidays. I have been to Italy, France, Spain, The Netherlands, Iceland, Malaysia, America, and New Zealand. Only one has been a beach holiday. The rest are mainly skiing or sight-seeing and we go somewhere at least once every year.

I have got a moped now and that gets me around. Sometimes I will just jump on the train so some of us might go off to Nairn to the beach or Dingwall to a football match.

I usually go shopping with friends. I quite often go to town with no plan to buy anything, but then may see something and will buy it. As far as clothes are concerned I prefer to go into a shop and see what things look like, rather than shop on line. Having said that, I do buy games and such on line.

I am fortunate in that I have a paper round delivering the Press and Journal (P&J) six times a week to around twenty houses. Wages work out on average £20 a week working out at £1 a house. I have friends who deliver free newspapers and they get 3p a paper so I think I have a good deal. I collect the money, fill in sheets and then give the money into P&J. I put the money into my account and it is mine - I don't have to give any to my mum!

I have applied for an apprenticeship working for an oil company working off shore. My plan is to get a Process Mechanic apprenticeship. I have been successful with the aptitude tests and the final interview but have been told I won't hear for ten weeks so I'll maybe know by the end of July. It is for a Process Operation Mechanic which involves going to college for two years and then going offshore on the rigs or to a refinery for nine months to a year. If I am successful I will start in September 2013. I will be seventeen then.

For me the biggest change in Inverness is probably the housing in Milton of Leys. Even since 2005 the housing numbers must have tripled.

I was nominated in late 2011 to run with the Olympic Torch by my mum due to my dedication, commitment and overall attitude towards sports. On the 11th June 2012 I carried the torch in Grantown on Spey, a nearby village. I carried the torch through the High Street and was greeted by a crowd of about two thousand people. I felt ecstatic, proud and overjoyed when running with the flame and it was an experience that will live with me forever.

6. Danyal Khalid & Struan Simpson

Danyal: I was born in Hong Kong, China in 1995 so I was still classed as British. I stayed there for ten months and then came to Inverness on 1st April 1996 – some April Fool eh!

Struan: I was born in Inverness in 1995. However, most of my family come from Caithness. My parents moved to Inverness about twenty years ago.

I started school at Central Primary School in 2000.

Danyal: I went to Central too and we were in the same class and have remained friends right through. Then when I was twelve I went on to the High School. For me the best thing about school were the teachers. They were so helpful and enthusiastic.

Struan: I would agree with Danyal. The teachers really motivate you and work hard to encourage you to do your best. When I was in the Sixth Form I did Advanced Higher Chemistry and had to go between the High School and another secondary school in Inverness and I felt the teachers in the other school don't work as hard at motivating you as those in the High School.

Danyal: The main activity I got involved in at school was music. They had a Jazz Band of which I was part. I played the guitar and it was really good fun. I found a new piping teacher through school that got me through my Standard and Higher grades in music. Music was definitely more my 'thing' than sport and the school accommodated my interest in music really well.

I have done busking in Inverness for a while now. It is great. I play the bagpipes. It's a really good way to meet new people and it is one of the easiest ways of making tax free money! I normally do an hour or an hour-and-a-half and can get up to £40 a go. I usually stand in one of the doorways of a closed shop or in between McDonald's and Poundland (which used to be Woolworths) in the High Street.

Struan: Like Danyal I was also involved in a lot of extra-curricular things mainly in music. I play the clarinet, so there were a lot of regional groups, such as orchestras and wind bands that work throughout the Highlands that I've been involved with for the past few years. At school, I was in both the Jazz band and Wind band. As a result I played in concerts and festivals which was fun. The school also ran a Leadership Group. This involved students throughout the school. The aim of the group was to develop decision making skills and things like that. I was part of that group until about fifth year. We usually helped to organise school discos and fundraising events for things like Comic Relief.

Struan: I am heading to Aberdeen University to study Chemistry. After that I am not really sure what my plans are. I want to see how well I do at university first and make a decision then.

Danyal: It costs a lot to go to university and I don't want the debt, so I have applied to Scottish and Southern Energy to do a four year electrical apprenticeship. I should hear whether I have a place in July. During the apprenticeship I will do day release at college and at the end of the four years I will be a certified electrician. I will then be able to go on to become a standardised qualified technician as well. If all this works out, I will perhaps pursue a part-time 'uni' course when I will hopefully be financially able to support myself.

Struan: Because music absorbs a lot of my life, I spend most of my leisure time relaxing. I spend a lot of time playing video games and using social websites such as Facebook and Twitter.

Danyal: In my spare time I play in two other bands outwith school. One is my church worship band where I play the guitar on Sunday mornings. I also belong to another band which plays in Coffee Affair coffee shop in Church Street each Saturday night. It is really exciting at the moment because we are writing our own music in a Scottish, blues style. I also volunteer in a bagpipe shop in town where I sit working on bagpipes and reeds which is great. Living out in Beauly means I can sit and listen to the pipe band that goes through there quite often which I enjoy.

When I was at school I walked or took the bus to get anywhere. When we moved to Beauly it meant going on the train or bus. The train is better because it is cheaper and more direct. The bus goes through all the little villages on route and can take ages. I now have my driving licence so I am saving up for a car and soon I will be causing havoc on the roads!!

Struan: When I was at school I walked. Even when I had to go between the two secondary schools I walked which was half an hour from where I lived. If I need to get further afield I would get the bus. I haven't been learning to drive because I think it is too expensive at the moment.

Danyal: I usually communicate with friends by texting from my mobile phone. When corresponding with family down south I send letters.

Struan: I don't have a phone and I don't think that affects the way I communicate. I still manage to get out with friends by messaging through social networks on the computer.

Danyal: For me I think the changes in Inverness have been the change in style of shops. It seems to be more panic buying and I feel there has been an explosion in mass consumerism. I mean before Woolworths was the biggest shop we had. Town now feels 'humungous' with the number of stores and stuff in them.

Struan: I would agree with Danyal. You don't see the small shops anymore. I remember going up to town with my mum and she would drag me into a number of shops; mainly the smaller shops where she knew the people who worked there and she would catch up on the news with them. Whereas now, if I go into town with her it feels like this would happen less.

I like Inverness because it does not seem too small or too large to me and I am still close to the people I know.

Danyal: I would agree what I love about Inverness are the people. They are so friendly and when on chance you meet people they seem pleased to see you. Even when I am busking if asked to move along because I am too loud it is done in a nice way. Generally people are friendly and really encouraging. It is great.

7. Caitlin Ball

I was born in Raigmore Hospital, Inverness in 1994. There are seven of us in our family, my mum, dad, three brothers, my sister and myself live in Lochardil and have always lived there. As a result I went to Lochardil Primary School which was only two minutes behind my house. When I think about primary school the thing that comes to mind is Sports Day - the sack race, egg and spoon race and the three-legged race.

When I reached twelve I went onto Inverness Royal Academy (IRA). We had a uniform which in theory was compulsory but some students just didn't bother to wear it. The school said it wanted us to wear the uniform for security reasons i.e. so staff could identify anyone who had no right to be in the school. I didn't really enjoy school. I wasn't a loner but I spent lots of time reading. I went home at lunch time until fourth year. After that I tended to stay in school with friends. My favourite subjects were music, history and art and all the fun subjects.

There were string and brass groups and in the last two years of school there was a folk group. I play the fiddle and hope to practise and play more and perhaps form a band. I took subjects such as Modern Studies, which was a combination of politics, the welfare system, all about what goes on in foreign countries: foreign policies, how voting works and basically how society has changed.

I stayed in school up to and including the sixth year and passed my exams. While at school I worked in the Oil & Vinegar shop in Union Street, then when I left I thought about going to 'uni' to train as a primary teacher. However I have changed my mind for now and I have got a job in Asda Inverness. Asda is a superstore and it sells almost everything. Along the back wall is a deli counter, fish counter, butchers counter and pizza counter. I started out as what is called a counter colleague making pizzas at the pizza counter. Then a month or so ago I moved to the front of the shop as Service Host where I make sure there are enough tills open and the cashiers have enough money. It is almost like a supervisor's role. I am hoping to apply for a manager's position.

The application process consisted of me going on line and getting and completing an application form, followed by a group session of twelve people to see how you interacted with each other. Having got through that, I was invited back for an informal one to one interview.

I believe dating is different today from what I understand it was years ago. It is much more informal and relaxed. For example, you might meet up as friends at the weekend in a bar and sit and chat, or go to the cinema. My boyfriend and I go for walks, out for dinner or just hang out together. We also play chess – in fact he taught me!

In terms of my leisure time I enjoy reading and watching DVDs. So for example, I will read a book and then if the book has been made into a film I will watch it. I also enjoy cycling and will ride along by the canal.

In terms of holiday, the only times I have been abroad are when I went to Italy with the school and when I went to Uganda to work with the Watoto children. I wanted to do some charity work so I went out to Uganda and stayed with a couple from my church who works with the Watoto children. It is such an amazing place and the children who live in the village where I stayed are all orphan children who are cared for by Watoto which is an International Christian Organisation. I was there for ten days. It was a brilliant experience.

As far as shopping is concerned I tend to go into Inverness, try clothes and then buy things if I like them. I may consider buying on line but so far that has not been my first option.

I think it is such a shame so many shops have disappeared. Although I am only the age I am I remember some of the small shops which were so nice and the introduction of the larger shops.

SUMMARY
Compare and Contrast
Life in the 1940s to life in 2013

It is hoped that through reading this book you have had memories awakened that had been long forgotten.

The stories have been recorded in chronological order from the oldest to the youngest in Part I while Part II starts with the youngest and ends with the oldest. This has been a deliberate decision to show that change in values, behaviour and society at large alter a day at a time. Reference to the Second World War was frequently referred to in both the stories and discussions showing how its impact was felt influencing the lives of individuals long after the war ended. Social changes and the advancement of technology as a direct result of the war has also had significant and major impact on everybody's lives and is evident as you read through this book.

It is easy to see that there are more stories from the older generation which capture the memories and changes in their lives. It also reflects what life was like in the '30s and '40s. People from different backgrounds were selected to show the similarities and differences that arose because of, and in spite of, where they came from. The content of Part II is inevitably more limited in comparison to the depth of information gathered from the older generation due to the fact that their personal experiences are limited, with life's long journey still to come. Some of the views that they expressed arise from aspirations and dreams for the future as opposed to real life experience.

During the workshops we looked at different topics each week and I have listed these below with the comments gathered to show the views and attitudes of those who attended. In some instances I have added comments from the stories which re-enforce points that were discussed. However, it would be wrong to think that this is all that the section is about. Also included are incidental comments that were made which are just as important in adding colour and interest. For example, with the older generation how they saw their families, how they see life now and then. The workshops encouraged group participation from both the young and old and it was encouraging to see how well both groups were willing to share and listen to one another.

We can be inclined to categorise people holding preconceived ideas of what we see them to be. Yet when preconceptions are challenged we realise they were not based on fact but rather generalisations. The workshops helped to break down such views. This project confirmed that there are some things that regardless of time remain constant, while other customs and values have changed enormously and will continue to evolve with successive generations. The discussions during the weekly workshops cemented these view and as you will see in each of the topics covered the similarities and differences will become obvious.

Play, technology and leisure
The first workshop, held on 15th March, met at the Inverness Museum. One of the activities was to look at toys from the 1930s and '40s which were passed round for the group to look at. The older generation recognised many of the toys, picking them up, playing with them, and talking with the young people about them. It stimulated memories and the pleasure on the faces of the older people as they reminisced was delightful to

see. On the other hand the young people were bemused by several of the toys only having been introduced to them during that session. They recognised the Yo-Yos and skipping ropes although the material and colour of the items were different from today. For example, the original Yo-Yo was made of tin. Today they are made of plastic and some have flashing lights. Skipping ropes today are brightly coloured and made of plastic, whereas back in the '40s they really were ropes with wooden handles. In the ensuing workshop, discussion about play continued. "Skipping, that is what I liked to do and we would sing skipping songs." **Rosa Finlayson.** "Yes I remember one skipping song started "The wind, the wind..." I also remember when I played throwing a ball against a wall I would sing "I, 2, 3 O'Leary..." **Joan Kelly**. "We played skipping and Yo-Yos." **Lucie Macintosh 15yr.**

Hop scotch was a popular game across the decades of the older people. It is known by different names depending on where people came from. Among the older generation it was a game they played often. However, the younger generation knew about the game and could recall it painted on the primary school playground but none of them admitted to playing it. For those who grew up in Inverness spending time down at the River Ness fishing, swimming, and watching the fishing boats hall all had been favourite pastimes. Playing at the canal was also another favourite place to go. None of the young people mentioned spending time down at the river or indeed along the canal.

The discussion and the stories highlighted key differences between the generations. The older people tended to play outside. Imaginary games were very popular such as houses, schools or shops using things from nature or brick-a-brac they found in fields to enhance the games. It was stressed that because they didn't have many toys they had to make their own entertainment and that was the best option. Street parties and concerts where very popular where children would sing, and recite poetry. Not only were street parties held for big events such as the Queen's Coronation but in places like Glasgow they were a regular event. Interestingly none of the young people involved in the project could recall attending a street party for any reason.

Overall, today's young people appear to spend less time outdoors playing unless it is organised play such as sports, skate boarding and cycling. They were more likely to stay indoors and play with soft toys, cars and Lego. Electronic games such as PlayStations and Xboxes are their current past times. It appeared more limiting than the earlier generations. Even the young history teacher who attended some of the workshops said she noticed how much had changed in terms of play in the past ten to twelve years.

"Today it seems to be all computer games. Fourteen year olds have iPads. Parents are scared to let children out to play whereas we had the freedom. The children seem to "do more" e.g. drama, dance, piano and guitar lessons, and Taekwondo." **Ann McSween.** "Video games, PlayStation and Xbox are easier to play with friends. You could buy a game for a fiver and then play it for 20 or 30 hours whereas you could spend £5/6 on a model or Action figure but you get bored with that quicker." **Alasdair MacRae 17yr.**

"I used to love making paper aeroplanes and holding competitions for them." **Rod Geddes.** "I was Fife Champion at Chess. This took up a large amount of my free time and I also used to enjoy playing 'Kick the Can' which was as form of hide and seek." **Peter Kelly.** "We played soldiers and barracks and conkers, and I remember playing board games such as "Snakes and Ladders, Ludo, Draughts, Tiddlywinks and Chess." **Peter Chisholm.**

"I used to collect and play with stuffed animals e.g. cuddly toys." **Lucie Macintosh 15yr.** "I spend most of my leisure time relaxing. I spend a lot of time playing video games and using social websites such as Facebook and Twitter." **Struan Simpson 18yr.**

"I lived in the country and only had my siblings and so we had to amuse ourselves. On one occasion I remember saying to my brother, "I am glad you are my brother because it means I won't have to marry you." When we would be playing we would use red toadstools as cakes." **Rosa Finlayson.** "We used to make mud pies for cakes." **Frances Forward.**

"As children we used to all play together outside and one game we played was where someone chalked out arrows on the path and everyone else had to follow the arrows. Then when you got to the end you had to kiss the boy when he found you." **Joan Kelly.** "We played football in the streets which was no problem because there were few cars to get damaged.

We played for hours and only came home to be fed." **Peter Chisholm.**

"Sunday nights we all played cards together and when I had a boyfriend then he joined in too." **Rosa Finlayson.** "Mums don't play with children today, at least not in the way they did in the past. They don't play family games." **Alex Harris.**

"The majority of young people talk about being on the Xbox or PlayStation by themselves. They tend to be playing the game alone online. I played in the garden. I think there has been a huge change in ten years." **Alex Harris.**

Organisations such as Brownies, and Boys Brigade played a big part in the lives of many of the older folk with activities being run by the organisations several times in a week and most weekends. When spoken about, it was obviously something people loved and were committed to. Boys and Girl's Brigades are still part of the lives of young people but they only attend once a week with a camp one weekend in the year. Although numbers are fewer today they remain considered good and fun activities.

"We had Brownies, Guides, Scouts, and Cadets which helped develop social skills." **Peter Chisholm.** "Yes we used to attend Brownies and Guides and we had weekends away camping. I remember we went to the Girl's Guildry." **Joan Kelly.**

School life
Listening to the stories and discussions it quickly became apparent that the core of the school curriculum has remained

fairly static. However, yet again the impact of technology and changes in social attitudes have significantly altered the method of delivery in education. For example, Smart Boards, computers and the acceptability of boys learning to cook a long side girls playing football. Nonetheless the general school day, the structure of lessons, uniform and such like remains fairly unaffected across primary and secondary education through the years. Another key change is sitting exams to get entry into secondary school. In past days students would sit the Eleven Plus or 'Quali' exam. This would determine whether they would pursue an academic, commercial or domestic course. It was more clearly defined from entry into the secondary school than what happens currently. Today there is no entry exam, the students tend to attend the secondary school closest to where they live. Also streaming in terms of ability and subject preference for career choices happens much later and is more flexible. Students stay on at school longer. In earlier days, students tended to leave school at fourteen or fifteen. Today the earliest age to leave is sixteen and even then the numbers who leave at that point tends to be the minority.

"I have always been interested in cooking. I watched all the various cooking programmes on TV such as Master Chef and they just inspired me to cook. Also my mum would teach me a trick or to and it all built up." **David Thomson 17yr.**

Wearing uniform also reflected change in society. In earlier years wearing uniform in primary school was not compulsory, in many instances this was due to lack of money and rationing during the war. However, wearing uniform in secondary school was seen as more important. This was in complete contrast to today. Of the young people who expressed a view all wore uniform in primary school whereas in secondary school overall it was far more lax.

"Everyone looks the same in uniform it gives a code of conduct and stops teasing." **Jason McClurg 16yr.** "Having said that, our head teacher would never send us home if we turned up in non-uniform and my parents would kill me if I didn't dress appropriately for school. They wouldn't let me out of the house wearing cropped tops and short skirts to school." **Lucie Macintosh 15yr.** "When I was in primary school I had a uniform and it was the norm to wear it. At high school it is not so strict, as long as you have one thing such as a tie or badge that represents the school that is fine." **Hamish Townshend. 16yr.** "We had a uniform which consisted of a navy blue gymslip, royal blue blazer, black stockings, white blouse, royal blue and gold tie. It was compulsory to wear it." **Betty MacRae.**

Discipline in school has changed considerably and by all accounts the young people who attended our workshops highlighted this. Interestingly, their view was the change had not necessarily been for the better.

"Bad behaviour gets attention. I feel teachers need to be more strict - bring back the belt! Teachers are not trained how to discipline pupils." **Jason McClurg 16yr.** "There is no follow through. The teachers need to mean what they say." **Lucie Mackintosh 15yr.**

"I feel there are times when teachers should be watching and engaging with the class more. All teachers use the computer in class now." **Rhona Weldon 15yr.** "I remember a Primary 7 teacher who would throw the board duster or chalk at you, or get her long board pointer, come round and slam it down on your desk." **Maureen Fraser.**

School lunch

The older generation tended to go home for lunch, in many instances because school dinners were not provided. It was the norm for mums to be at home and so children would go home and mum would have lunch ready – a plate of soup and such like. Children lived close to primary school and so they could walk there and back easily. Today with so many mums working and children living further away from the school there isn't an option to go home at lunchtime. In secondary school it appears that common practice is to have school lunch or go out of school and visit the local supermarket buying sandwiches or whatever and then return to school for the afternoon. Young people seem to have spare cash to do this whereas in earlier years parents did not have the money to give to the children for them to get food in that way.

Overall the young people said they enjoyed school and for most it is a positive experience. For some of the older generation this was not the case, it was the worst time in their lives. "I hated primary school, teachers terrorised me. I was told I was a dunce. I remember being given six of the best." I loved the High School though. I felt I was treated as a person but I remember the whole class got strapped because one person forgot their sewing box." **Frances Forward.**

Another interesting point of discussion was about school activities and outings. One could be forgiven for thinking that after-school activities or school outings were a more recent inclusion in the curriculum but that is not the case. "Sports were organised in the lunch time and netball games on Saturday mornings." **Madelyn Cruickshank.** "We lived in the country which meant we needed to get a bus and so we didn't tend to go to anything after school. Kids in town had opportunity to go to the baths and activities such as the Guides. Because we lived in the country we listened to the radio when we got home. For example Radio Luxemburg, The Goons and Monty Python were favourites." **Frances Forward.** "I am currently at school and we have clubs during the lunch break and after school. They are subject driven." **Rhona Weldon 15yr** "The High School has a Jazz band and a Group for S2 and above where an external company comes into the school for a day working with us on Leadership skills." **Amber Ness 15yr.** "I go to drama at Eden Court which is paid for by the school." **Ben Carter 15yr.**

"I remember going on a school holiday to Wales in the last two years of school. We went rock climbing, abseiling, walking and I fell in love with the Instructor! My second holiday was to Geneva for one week." **Madelyn Cruikshank.** "Twenty of us went to Germany on a boat. We were about 14/15 years old. It was for three weeks. We had to get the train to London, a train from London to the boat. When we stayed in Munich we had bunk beds with duvets and were given black rye bread to eat. There was also a vending machine which I had never seen before. We had to wear tartan skirts." **Frances Forward.** "In the High School we have activity days for students in S1-3. These consist of various options. For example, go-karting, going to the cinema, making mosaics or going to Landmark for the day. My friends and I had the opportunity to go to Paris for a week. We left Sunday night at 10pm on the bus and only got four hours sleep. We watched 'Back to the Future' films. I have also been to some activity centres such as Abernethy for a working week. We were given study time to prepare us for our exams and future courses at Uni and student life. We had to prepare our own food!" **Jason McClurg 16yr.**

Employment

It is noteworthy that when young people left school in the 1930s and 1940s they appeared to leave school one day and started in a job the next. This is very unlike current young people. The gap in time between leaving school and taking up employment is much wider. The application process is more formal and in general applying for and starting a job can take weeks. Going onto university after leaving school is a more popular choice for today's young people than was in the past. The reintroduction of the option of pursuing apprenticeships is becoming a preferred option once more.

"I started work at sixteen. I worked down the coal mine as an Appliances Electrician. When you started you had someone who taught you what you needed to know. He was called a

Journeyman. The apprenticeship lasted five years. You got a certificate and attended Mining School at Cowdenbeath two days a week during that apprenticeship. I got paid £3 a week. I kept 5/- and the rest went into the house." **Peter Kelly.** "I left school at fourteen and worked in the laundry. The floor Manager taught me what to do. I gave all my wages to my mum and she gave me pocket money." **Jean Urquhart.** "My first job was while I was still at school. I worked in the local bakers and I waitressed in a café. **Madelyn Cruikshank.** In days past many left school at the age of fourteen and went into work, whereas today the earliest students leave school is sixteen.

"I have applied for an apprenticeship working for an oil company working off shore. My plan is to get a Process Mechanic apprenticeship. I have been successful with the aptitude tests and the final interview but have been told I won't hear for 10-11 weeks so I'll maybe know by the end of July." **Finlay MacLeod 16yr.** "I wanted to be a cabinet maker but there were no vacancies. I started work as a message boy with the buses and I asked the boss if I could get an apprenticeship to be a mechanic. I also went on a PAB (Pre-apprenticeship Builder Course). This was to give me a taster of different jobs in the trade." **Rod Geddes.** Many young people today consider university as an option and indeed take a gap year where they can travel first before deciding on their future career.

The older generation automatically handed over their weekly wages to their parents and were then given 'pocket money' in return. This was something today's young generation could not comprehend. Their opinion was that the money they earned belonged to them, contributing a percentage to the home when they commenced full-time employment.

"My first job was working Saturdays on the counters in Woolies. I got paid 10/- for the day. I had to pay 1/6^d for the bus fare, 1/9^d for the pictures and with the rest I remember one time buying a skirt." **Rosa Finlayson.**

"I have a paper round delivering the Press & Journal six times a week to around 20 houses. Wages work out on average £20 a week – that's £1 a house." **Finlay MacLeod 16yr.**

A stark difference was the number of women who had dreams of a career. Yet, either because it was considered 'not suitable' for a woman, or because it was expected that the girl would leave school and stay in the family home to take on the caring role of the family as needed, they had so often to sacrifice their personal ambition. Although it would be wrong to say this does not happen today, views expressed implied it would not be the choice or expectation of the majority of young women.

"When women got married they had to leave work and up until the 1960s women got paid 25% less than men." **Peter Chisholm.** "A man was seen as the 'bread winner'. Girls were not encouraged to have careers. The key jobs you were told about were: nursing, banking and secretarial. There was no career advice." **Ann McSween.** "Women were expected to support men in their career." **Madelyn Cruikshank.** "I was in a co-ed class and I was expected to go on to university but my parents told me to 'go and earn a living'." **Maureen Fraser.**

"I worked in the Central Hotel in Glasgow, also in Gleneagles, and Turnberry. I did what was known as Silver Service. I earned £3 a week and all the money went into the house. I had to buy my uniform before I started the job." **Ann McSween.** "I worked for Alexander Buses, but before that, when I was about twelve I had two jobs - a milk boy with a horse and cart in the mornings and delivery boy delivering parcels after school. When I started work on the buses and I got 16/- for forty-five hours a week and again all the money went to my mother and she gave me some spending money." **Rod Geddes.**

How to get a Job

"I filled in a form, took a math exam, went to Cowdenbeath Mining School to see the different trades and chose what I wanted. In 1963 many jobs moved to paying monthly rather than weekly which was a struggle and a huge shift for low paid earners. Up until the early 1970s the majority of people still got paid their wages in cash. The wages would be handed out in a brown envelope with a transparent top so you could count the notes. Inside would be the pay slip. Overtime was paid in arrears." **Peter Kelly.** "As a trainee nurse I got paid £7 a month. I lived in the Nurses' Home and got food and uniform over and above. I was expected to buy my shoes and stockings." **Rosa Finlayson.**

"When I was working for the mine I was not given sick pay but when I worked for Rolls-Royce they did pay me. I was shocked. In fact one time when one of my children was very sick the company arranged for a plane and taxi to take me from up north to the hospital." **Peter Kelly.** "I only got sick pay when I became salaried not when I worked as a fitter on the buses. I was treasurer of the Sick Fund. Everyone contributed to this fund. The rise in the unions in the late '40s helped change working practices, including maternity pay. The introduction of leave and paternity leave is a good thing as it encourages the men to get involved with the family." **Rod Geddes.**

Length of time in a job

"I worked thirty-nine years and seven months for the same company." **Peter Chisholm.**
I worked twenty-two years working for NHS and my husband has worked thirty-three years for the NHS." **Frances Forward.** "I worked forty-four years for Rolls-Royce." **Peter Kelly.** "My husband worked forty years in the Royal Mail, but contracts have changed today e.g. temporary contracts, part-time and some people have two or three jobs at one time. Global companies and mergers have resulted in people having to re-apply for their own job. There is a general lack of permanency today." **Madelyn Cruickshank.**

It is recognised in today's society that employees in virtually any form of employment will change employer and indeed path of career at least three times in a working life. This is very different to past generations where loyalty and remaining in the same type of work first chosen was what was expected. It

210

also had much to do with the expectations and direction of the parents.

Love and Romance

Dating and marriage was a fascinating subject to discuss not only with those interviewed for the book but by those attending the workshops. This subject reflected the biggest change in values and society's beliefs. In Part I of the book many describe going to dances, dressing up, and being walked home. It all has a romantic feel to the whole experience. Weddings were not lavish but still beautiful with lovely dresses, receptions in a hotel and a short but happy honeymoon. In contrast, relationships with the young of today appear to be less formal, with a more casual approach. They just 'hang out' together, talking via social networks or mobile 'phones and weddings being either not on the agenda or quite extravagant. The days of being asked out by the boy, going to a specific occasion and being taken home appear to be things of the past.

"I hope to meet someone when I am older." **Lucie Mackintosh. 15yr.** "When we were at Inverness High School there were two couples in my year that met and married." **Rosa Finlayson.** "Oh I wouldn't kiss in the street. I know people do it but I wouldn't. When you are interested in someone you just text or phone them." **Amber Ness 15yr.** "Meeting someone used to be face- to-face but now it's 'getting together' though social networking." **Becky Seath.** "We never played with girls. We would walk on the other side of the road. My sisters would even get dressed to

211

hang out the washing in case they saw a boy!" **David MacMaster.** "Some young people like old fashioned ways." **Amber Ness 15yr.**

Discussion around the subject of gay relationships and living together proved to be the most polarised in terms of views and outlook as expressed in the quotes below.

"Love is love whether the relationship is male and female or male and male, female and female." **Lucie Mackintosh 15yr.** "I know many people who don't approve." **Rosa Finlayson.**
"I don't think it is an ideal situation for children to be raised in a gay relationship but better that than living in a heterosexual chaotic one." **Maureen Fraser.** "We are all born with the ability to respond to love. I am over fifty years married. Love is a gift - a bond." **David McIver.** "I remember some chap coming up to me and asking if I had twenty minutes free to be a witness at his wedding. I had never seen him before. I did it and I have never seen him since!" **Peter Chisholm.**

Shopping

This discussion was interesting in that the young people did not have as much to say as I thought they would. Food shopping was not something they related to, that was carried out by the parents and they just reaped the benefits. The older generation tended to be more involved, by being expected to go and get the shopping. Some of the change is linked more to the fact of how people do their food shopping. In days past food shopping was done daily due to having no fridges and freezers and seen much more as an outing or event. Also there were not the large supermarkets where people today will go and get everything

212

they need in one store at one time. Many folk relayed stories of grocer and milk vans and carts coming round the doors and people would send the children with a list to the van to get certain items. The nearest we have of that today is the supermarket Shop an' Drop service! "Inverness used to have loads of individual shops... You didn't have to go out of town to retail parks there was none of these big shops." **Angy MacDiarmid**. "Shopping was done near enough on a daily basis and when my mother went shopping she used to get dressed and always wore a hat!" **Tina Foss**. "There were several grocer type shops around and smaller shops that had basic items. I remember my mother would send me to Hettie's.... to get a loaf – a wrapped loaf because Hettie's cat sat in the window and had free range of the shop!" **Peter Chisholm**. "I would knock on the window of a particular lady's house and she would sell me a wee bit of toffee." **Cath Martin**. "My mum bought groceries from a van that came to the house." **Anne Lyle**. "Grant Street was great for doing the shopping. There was everything in the one street. The Co-operative, the Shoe Maker's, the Post Office, three butchers, a furniture shop, and Stevie Fraser's shop where he sold just milk." **Jean Murray**.

Shopping for clothes was interesting. Young people said "We shop in Topshop and shops like that in Eastgate or shop online." **Lucie Mackintosh, Amber Ness, Rhona Weldon. All 15yr.** The young men tended only to shop as they needed something and although they would shop online for music and things like that, when it came to clothes they still tend to go into town. "I don't do a lot of shopping. I shop when I need it. When I do I come into town so I can check things fit." **Hamish Townshend. 16yr.** The young women expressed the view they would shop online for clothes but more often than not they shopped in Eastgate. Due to the age group involved, buying their own clothes was not generally a key thing. Parents still provided. "I don't do much shopping. I tend to tell my mum what I want and she gets it for me." **Lesley Maciver.** However for the few that had after school jobs their money tended to go on clothes and entertainment which was a stark contrast to the older generation where even doing after school jobs their money was first given into the home. "I remember when I was at school getting a job as a message boy ... and I got 12/6^d a week. My mother would take 10/ and I would get 2/6^d." **Ian Fraser.**

With the older generation the impact of the war and the use of coupons played a central part in all shopping. Obviously this is not the case today. Another difference is the use of credit. This was not even in the thinking of the older generation. People saved up for anything they wanted and only bought the items when they had the money. In many instances people had an account with a specific grocer and would buy the shopping during the week but would always go to the shop at the end of the week and clear any outstanding bills. Many of the older generation involved in the project stressed that even today that is how they operate.

"During and just after the war we had to use coupons to buy clothes so that meant you couldn't just go out and buy things anytime." **Ann McSween.** "I remember you got extra coupons for school uniforms if you got too tall or big." **Rod Geddes.**

"We would make and mend our clothes." **Maureen Fraser.** "We wouldn't dream of making our own clothes, that's SO funny." **Lucie Mackintosh, Amber Ness, Rhona Weldon. All 15yr.** "It is very acceptable to buy clothes from charity shops because it is unique, after all it is important to wear the right clothes on the right occasion." **Amber Ness 15yr** "I enjoy shopping. In fact I shop every weekend when I am not at work…. Most of my money goes on clothes and shoes." **Lisa Stacey 16yr.** "It seems to me we have a throw away culture. People don't want to buy things that last. That is so different from the way things were for us." **Angy MacDiarmid.**

Health

"To me when I think of the word 'health' I think of hospitals, doctors, and getting better." **Lucie Mackintosh 15yr.** "I think in the end how healthy you are, is determined by your genes." **Madelyn Cruikshank.** "I think there are different types of health - fitness and mental state and so on." **Ben Carter 15yr.**

"I remember the Isolation Hospital at Culduthel. People with illnesses like T.B. or Scarlet Fever would be kept there. Visitors were only allowed to visit by standing outside and looking through the window at the patient." **Frances Forward.** "Father got a bill from the dentist but he couldn't pay it so he tore it up! We would go to the chemist and get treatment and a prescription. **Peter Kelly.** "I remember we would pay the dentist 'in kind' with some eggs." **Frances Forward.** "My mother would

215

give us cod liver oil in orange juice every day." **Madelyn Cruickshank**. "We were given malt every day." **Rosa Finlayson**.

"The school nurse used to come into school and check your height, weight and sight." **Lucie Mackintosh 15yr**. "We used to be given syrup of figs every Saturday night." **Jean Urquhart**. "It's 'five-a-day' with cereal, fruit and yoghurt for me now." **Rosa Finlayson**.

"I remember being taken to the RNI to have my tonsils out. There were six of us sitting on a trolley, towels round us all waiting for this procedure and then getting home that night." **Peter Chisholm**. "I was in hospital for three nights when I got my tonsils out and my parents didn't get to visit me." **Madelyn Cruickshank**.

Travel

Today, young people have so many opportunities to travel and it is good to see where they go and the experiences they encounter whether it is through school trips or with family. The type of accommodation and amount of time on holiday may be different but opportunities have always been available.

"There were loads of cycling clubs - often a place to meet a husband! I learned to ride a big bike when I was ten." **Ann McSween**. "I travelled for miles round Cannich. My father bought a police cycle and was paid one penny per mile when he used it on police business." **Peter Chisholm**. "Cars changed things. You always bought second hand cars and they always needed fixing!" **Madelyn Cruickshank**. "I remember getting the milk train at 4: 30am and the train had all individual carriages." **Ann McSween.** "I remember being at the train station and their being a fire in the waiting room." **Joan Kelly.** "I remember when I lived in Kent going with some friends on Eurostar to Paris for lunch!" **Madelyn Cruickshank.** "I remember my first time in a car was as a flower girl at a wedding. I was six years old." **Joan Kelly.** "I stopped cycling when I was twelve." **Nestor Beveridge 17yr.** "I enjoy riding around on my motor bike having easy access to hit the roads." **David Thomson 17yr.**

"I lived in a tenement in Glasgow and we didn't have a car. I remember the horse and cart coal lorry coming. On one occasion in 1945 a cousin came to visit. He had a car and there were about forty children looking and admiring it." **Ann McSween.**

"I learned to drive when I was in the Army and I got my licence from that". **Peter Chisholm.** "Driving lessons cost £1 per lesson and the new motorways brought in new signs that you had to learn." **Ann McSween.** "Most practice in the car was with my father and you didn't have a theory test! You had to learn hand signals and the indicators were orange and came out from the side of the car." **Madelyn Cruickshank.** "I now have my driving licence so I am saving up for a car and soon I will be causing havoc on the roads!!" **Danyal Khalid 18yr.**

"I remember flying from Heathrow London to Glasgow. You just walked through a hut right through onto the road for the bus." **Ann McSween.** "Who remembers Inverness runway being on the grass at the Longman?" **Madelyn Cruickshank.** "I was one of eight passengers who had the opportunity to go on a flight around Inverness for 2/6^{d} in 1938." **Peter Kelly.** "Just after the war I flew with an engineer who was lodging with my mother. We were the only two passengers." **Rod Geddes.**

Holidays and Outings

"We would go to North Kessock, take a frying pan and fry sausages. We would go by bus and ferry." **Peter Chisholm.** "I remember paddling in the water at North Kessock." **Jean Urquhart.** "We used to go on a bus trip to Rosemarkie. We would go swimming, gather whelks, boil them and then eat them." **Rod Geddes.** "Sunday we went on a walk to the cemetery wearing our 'Sunday Best'." **Jean Urquhart.**

"We went to Rothesay and Millport. We hired a holiday home for the 'Fair Fortnight' in July. All our family would get together. My mother was one of fourteen so it was just like 'The Broons'. We would invariably meet folk we knew who were also on holiday. We would have street parties. Someone would play the squeeze box - good fun that didn't cost any money." **Ann McSween.** "We didn't go on holiday. For me a holiday was time off school. At fourteen years old I went with the Air Force cadets to Feltwell near Kings Lynn." **Peter Kelly.**

"We were evacuated to Troon and later on we went back there for holidays. We went to Butlins in Skegness. We also went to Dunoon and rented a house. We went by train and ferry and took a pram packed with linen for the beds." **Maureen Fraser.** "We went to Cannich to my Aunt's. We had to pump for water.

218

We milked cows, collected eggs, fished and snared rabbits. We did lots of cycling round Strathglass, and Glen Affric - approximately forty miles a day." **Peter Chisholm.**

"I would go to my uncle's farm - Drumaine Farm. I helped with the harvest and chopped sticks. It was a working holiday. I started this at fourteen. I didn't get paid or given any pocket money - just accommodation. I then discovered girls and we would go camping and cycling to Glen Affric." **Rod Geddes.** "When we moved to the South of England (Paddock Wood) we used to go hop picking. Londoners spent three weeks hop picking to earn a little bit of money." **Madelyn Cruickshank.**

"We go on holiday round the UK – Devon, London, Cardiff, Scotland and we stay in hotels." **Rhona Weldon 15yr.** "As a family, we go all round the UK but we have also been to the USA, Spain, Coast of Africa, Ibiza and we stay in hotels." **Ben Carter 15yr.** "In 1951 we went to Epping Forest. We had interesting holidays. Mum dyed her blouse green – it rained – I ended up green. I also went to International Camp. Children today go on PGL holidays otherwise known as 'Parents Get Lost' trips. These are run in the UK and continent such as the South of France." **Maureen Fraser.** "Twice I went to Burntisland. There were six of us and we stayed in a chalet. We went by bus. I remember being about five or six and it was the first time I saw the sea - I was astounded. My father died when I was thirteen years old and from then on I went youth hostelling and cycled to Glen Devon which was about thirty miles." **Joan Kelly.** "I cycled two hundred miles to Scotch Corner and then got the train home."

Peter Kelly. I got my first passport in 1949 and when I got it I hitch hiked to France." **Peter Chisholm.**

"When on holiday I would buy presents to take home such as fridge magnets for everyone! It was the 'done' thing." **Frances Forward.** "People don't tend to send postcards anymore but I like to send them and I like to receive them. **Peter Chisholm.**

Events of different kinds
"The Highland Gathering is an event for all ages. All sorts of things happening such as tug of war, tossing the caber, highland dancing, pipe bands." **Peter Chisholm.** "There is also Hogmanay also known as Auld Year's night or New Year's Eve. In Scotland at midnight everything begins, in England the night ended." **Madelyn Cruickshank.** "I remember Halloween, we would all dress up, go to people's doors and given an apple. It was called 'Guising'. You would be expected to sing a song or say a poem and I remember we used crepe paper to make skirts." **Ann McSween.** "You always went to people you knew. I think the USA has influenced the Trick o' Treat and it is not safe now." **Madelyn Cruikshank.**

"There is The Black Isle Show which is an agricultural show and takes place every year. It has become a really big event. Around the same time Moy Fair is held which is about shooting and fishing for the county set - a middle class event." **Rod Geddes.** "Today there is Rock Ness and Belladrum Festival. Belladrum is more of a family event. It is for all ages and is good for the economy, while Rock Ness is brilliant but more for young people who are into music". **Ben Carter 15yr.**

"I remember Jazz nights at the Philharmonic in Glasgow. They were wonderful! I also remember Ella Fitzgerald and Louis Armstrong performing at the Odeon in Glasgow in 1959." **Maureen Fraser.** "Big Bands came to the Caley Hotel in the late 1950s." **Rosa Finlayson.** "All the big bands and stars came to Glasgow. It was great." **Ann McSween.** "Belladrum and Rock Ness are where concerts happen now." **Ben Carter 15yr.** "A memorable event for me would be the 'Up Helly Aa' festival in Shetland. It happens every year. It is amazing." **Lesley Mciver.**

"Ranger Sports held International sports events and in the mid-1950s. Chris Chataway broke the world record there. Celtic provided similar events." **Maureen Fraser.** "We were invited to attend the Queen's Garden Party in 1985 at Holyrood Palace. Our daughter was included in the invite because at that time it was the custom for daughters aged 16-21, who were considered eligible for marriage, to be included in the invitation." **Madelyn Cruickshank.**

"On Coronation Day we had a street party. Lord and Lady Burton had a Coronation party picnic and the children were given a Coronation mug." **Frances Forward.** "I remember getting a silver spoon from school in commemoration of the coronation." **Madelyn Cruickshank.**

"My son received the Golden Fiddler Award and played at the Royal Albert Hall in London. He also played the fiddle in a concert in Nova Scotia at the age of twelve." **Rosa Finlayson.** "A big event for me is 'Singing for Pleasure', our times together every week and the concerts we do." **Frances Forward.** "We are in the school jazz and wind bands and we perform at music festivals every year at Eden Court. It is competitive and the High School won this year! **Lucie Mackintosh, Rhona Weldon, Amber Ness. All 15yr.** "We have been doing the Duke of Edinburgh Award which is promoted in school but the activities take place out of school hours. We have to do activities to develop skills such as long walks and camping in remote areas.   It is a recognised and prestigious award." **Ben Carter 15yr.** "I remember winning a ticket along with three others to go and watch a slideshow about Edmund Hillary and Sherpa Tenzing climbing Mount Everest." **Maureen Fraser.** "I remember I was in the Army and based in Hampshire when I had my twenty-first and receiving a parcel from home which consisted of a haggis and a note saying "I'm sure the cook can heat it up for you!" **Peter Chisholm.**

"For me a big event was celebrating my sixtieth birthday at the Muirtown Hotel. It was a surprise given to me by my family." **Rod Geddes.** "For us it was a trip to Rome for our twenty-fifth wedding anniversary arranged by our family." **Joan & Peter Kelly.** "For me it was being in hospital in labour on my twenty-first!" **Ann McSween.** "A big event for me is coming. When I am eighteen I will open the bottle of champagne I was given for my fifteenth birthday!"

Ben Carter 15yr. "A big event for me was First Communion which was done through the school." **Peter Kelly.** "For me it was when I carried the Olympic torch in Grantown on Spey in June 2012. It was an experience that will live with me forever." **Finlay MacLeod.** "Retirement at fifty-five was seen as a big event In the

1980/90s. It was promoted as the best thing ever giving lots of time to enjoy leisure time." **Madelyn Cruickshank.**

And finally

Eight months ago, when asked to commission the Golden Stories, I had no idea what a store of priceless recollections would be forthcoming from people who have spent so much of their lives here in the Highlands as well as those who are young or more recently moved into the area. Through the intervening years some of those interviewed moved away either by choice or through circumstance, but each has been almost inextricably drawn back to the place of their origins and family roots. Time after time those interviewed express sentiments saying that the Highlands, but mainly Inverness, is "home", "a place of peace and quiet", "beauty" and so on and so forth. Few were glad to leave and all were happy to return. It has been easy to see the attraction of such an idyllic part of the world. However, it is something much much deeper than mere sightseeing that makes Inverness such a magnet for so many people. It is about a way of life, a sense of community that is, in so many ways, unique to the area. It is also about something almost intangible that cannot easily be set down in words, though I have tried very hard to capture the essence of the thoughts, feelings, values, aspirations and memories of those whom I have been privileged to meet.

More than fifty people have given of their time, and shared their lives and that is what I believe to be the essence of the success of this venture. It is the warmth, the affection and the humour that is conveyed as they speak of what has been and what is for some, still to come, that makes this collection of golden memories such a delight to recall and to read. It is about ordinary, yet at the same time extraordinary stories of real lives and adventures that do not skate over what some may deem as life's mistakes, but rather embrace them seeing each one as part of life's richer tapestry.

Personally, I have learnt so much both in terms of the modern history of Highland life, as well as its language and jargon and I know I am the richer for having had the experience of writing about it. I thank each and every one interviewed for giving me a glimpse into their past, and a fore-taste of things that may well be as we travel through the 21st century. One thing is certain, it has been a pleasure to have met such a diverse group of charming characters who have contributed to this remarkable collection that make up Golden Stories.

Liz Syred
Editor

Glossary

❖ **Archie** - if you think you are Archie, you think you are someone special.

❖ **Bairns** – children.

❖ **Beddies** - another name for hop scotch.

❖ **Bees-knees** - excellent, high standard.

❖ **Boom** - this was to keep the enemy submarines from coming in.

❖ **Brose** - was oatmeal, salt and pepper and then boiling water over it.

❖ **Burn -** small stream or brook.

❖ **Caj** - modern abbreviation for casual.

❖ **Candled -** passing the eggs over 'strong Lights' in order to pick out 'blood spots' or 'meat spots' or 'fine cracks' and also can tell the age of the egg by the size of the 'air sac' at the broad end of the egg.

❖ **Catty** - This was a game where you had a piece of wood pointed at each end, marked one to four. You would put it over a hole in the ground then flick with a stick and if it landed towards you, you got points and would get an extra turn.

❖ **Clear our feet** - get out of debt.

❖ **Clootie Dumpling** - A traditional pudding made with flour, breadcrumbs, dried fruit, suet, sugar and spice and sometimes golden syrup. Ingredients are mixed well into a dough, then wrapped up in a floured cloth, placed in a large pan of boiling water and simmered for a couple of hours before being lifted out and dried before the fire or in an oven.

❖ **Communion Season** - is a three day event held in the Presbyterian Free Church which is comparable to the observance of the Passover.

❖ **Didnae** - did not.

- ❖ **Dog Cart** - a flat cart with a board across it which you sat on.
- ❖ **Doll's Eye Switchboard** - a manual exchange switchboard used in offices. The operator would plug in connections allowing people to speak to each other. It was possible to have a three way conversation.
- ❖ **Donkey Stones** - a type of scouring block, used mostly in the mill towns of the North of England to clean stone steps.
- ❖ **Dripping on bread** - juice of the beef which is left from the Sunday joint to be spread on bread with a little bit of salt to taste. Often given as a meal in itself.
- ❖ **Dutch** - a couple going out for an evening together and instead of the man paying for the lady, both would pay for themselves.
- ❖ **Dux medal -** in Scotland, Australia, New Zealand, Iceland and South Africa the dux medal is the title given to the top student in academic/sporting achievement.
- ❖ **Easy oasy** - relaxed, care free.
- ❖ **Expatriate – sometimes shortened to ex-pat -** a person who is voluntarily absent from home or country.
- ❖ **Fair Fortnight or Trades Fortnight** - it is when factories close and all tradesmen take two weeks summer holiday, usually in the month of July.
- ❖ **First Footing** - it is the visiting of friends and family immediately after midnight on 31st December and sees the Scots going from house to house to welcome in the New Year. The First-Foot in the house traditionally is a dark, handsome male carrying a piece of coal, whisky, Scottish shortbread and black bun - a rich dark fruitcake encased in pastry.
- ❖ **Flitting –** to move from one place to another

- **Gillie of the river** - a man or a boy who acts as an attendant on a fishing, fly fishing, hunting, or deer stalking expedition, primarily in the Highlands.
- **Girls Guildry** - was a Church-centred organisation founded in Scotland in 1900. It provided programmes for four age groups. Its activities were aimed at helping girls to become mature Christian women. The movement was interdenominational and international, with a strong emphasis on service to others. Membership at the time of Union was 35,000.
- **Girning** – to complain fretfully or peevishly
- **Glums, The** – T.his was a British Comedy broadcast on radio from 1948-1960.
- **Goon Show, The** - This was a British Comedy Radio Programme originally broadcast on BBC Home Service from 1951-1960. It is said that Price Charles was a great fan as a child.
- **Higher** - one of the national school-leaving certificate exams and university entrance qualifications of the Scottish Qualifications Certificate (SQC).
- **International Camp** - Camp started in 1949 after the Second World War to bring young people together from different parts of Europe and beyond to re-establish positive relations doing sporting activities.
- **Jacks** - it is an ancient game still played today. It consists of a rubber ball, and metal or plastic objects (jacks). Players take it in turn to bounce the ball off the ground, then pick up jacks, and then catch the ball before it bounces for a second time.
- **Lady's Choice dance** - it was a dance in the evening where the ladies got to ask the men to dance.
- **Messages** - another name for shopping.

- **Mod** - A festival of Scottish Gaelic song, arts and culture. It is a choral event in Gaelic, both solo and choirs, and traditional music.
- **Munros** – The Munros are the highest of Scotland's mountains, 282 mountain tops named after the man who first catalogued them, Sir Hugh Munro. The Munros are among the finest mountains in Scotland.
- **'O' Level** - a subject-based qualification part of the General Certificate of Education (GCE) in England. It was introduced as part of British educational reform in the 1950s.
- **Peevers** - otherwise known as hop scotch.
- **PGL holidays** - PGL stands for Peter Gordon Lawrence who set up this company in 1950s offering young people adventure holidays all over the UK and Continent.
- **Piece** - a sandwich.
- **Pipe clay -** is pale, whitish clay which forms a ductile paste with water. It is traditionally used for all sorts of polishing and whitening purposes as well as for making tobacco pipes and pottery.
- **Poke** - paper bag.
- **Prefabs -** were houses built after the war to house people whose houses had been destroyed. They were considered to be temporary accommodation with a life span of ten years. However, many were still inhabited for many years after the war. All prefabs came pre-decorated in magnolia, with gloss-green on all additional wood, including the door trimmings and skirting boards.
- **Prom** - dance at the end of the school year where students dress up and celebrate the end of the school year.
- **Scrumping** - action of stealing apples from an orchard.
- **Shieling -** a summer dwelling once common in a wild or lonely place in the hills/mountains. Usually very sparse with only a bed, Tilly lamp, table.

- ❖ **Siesta** - Traditionally a siesta lasts for half an hour and it is a time to have a sleep.
- ❖ **Silver Service** - it is the name given to a specific way of serving meals, traditionally used in some more formal settings. The rule of serving was always serve to the left. The name of this method comes from the fact that, traditionally, the entire cutlery, plates and serving equipment was made of silver.
- ❖ **Show of Presents** - this happens usually about a week before the wedding. The mother of the bride normally hosts the evening, providing tea and cakes. Female wedding guests, friends and neighbours are invited to look at the presents the couple have received and some guests may bring gifts which are then opened for everyone to see.
- ❖ **Skitchie** - flat stone used in the game of hop scotch.
- ❖ **Smiddy** – a blacksmith's shop.
- ❖ **Snapchat** - is a photo messaging application which enables users to take photos, record videos, add text and drawings, and send them to their contacts. The clips or photos sent are known as "snaps". Users set a time limit for how long recipients can view their snaps, ranging from up to ten seconds to as little as one second. This was first released in 2011.
- ❖ **Stair heid** –head of the stairs.
- ❖ **Swedish House** - was an all-timber house. The Swedish government gave a gift of one hundred timber-framed houses to Scotland between 1945/46.
- ❖ **Tackety Boots** - strong leather boots which had steel tackets in the soles which could be replaced and saved the leather from wearing out. It made them extra strong and gave good grip especially in the farm fields.
- ❖ **Tam O'Shanter** – A narrative poem by Robert Burns in 1790.

- ❖ **Tattie Holidays** - usual a two week holiday in October when farmers would harvest their crop of potatoes. Children and families would go along to the local farm and help with the harvesting.
- ❖ **Teuchter** pronounced "**choochter**" this was (is) a contemptuous name given by a Lowland Scot to someone from the Highlands, especially someone who speaks Gaelic.
- ❖ **Tied House** - that went with a workers job.
- ❖ **Tithe** - is a one-tenth part of something, paid as a contribution to a religious organisation.
- ❖ **Young and Old event** - a dance/party held at a local hotel where parents would bring along their children and teenagers for an evening's entertainment.
- ❖ **Uni** - short for university.

Some examples of differences in Dialect and Language

- **Aken** - I know
- **A kent** - I knew
- **Baffies** - slippers
- **Come away ben the hoose** - come away into the house
- **C'mon get aff** - come on get off
- **Lavy, cludgy, loo, WC, Jinky, bog** - toilet
- **Derbac** - soap (black) or lifebuoy soap for washing hair
- **Sook** - a comforter a piece of material
- **Sooking up** - getting a favour from someone
- **Oxster** - armpit
- **Dunny** - back court
- **Wally Close** - tiles half way up the close
- **Simmit** - vest
- **I bide** - I live
- **How** - instead of why

Money comparison for then and now

Original Date	Old Price	Equivalent price today
1930s	6^d	£1.30
1932 (wages)	7/-	£19.94
1936 (house)	£600	£33,450.00
1940	2/6^d	£5.60
1945	£1.00	£35.41
1947	5/-	£8.03
1948 (wages)	£1.8/-	£41.77
1948	10/-	£14.92
1949	4/6^d	£6.52
1949	10^d	£1.22
1950	£3.00	£84.35
1953	2/6^d	£2.83
1953	10/-	£11.46
1954	£40	£898.60
1955	£3.00	£64.58
1956 (boat fare to NZ)	£100	£2,048.00
1958 (bus fare)	2½^d	£0.19
1960	30/-	£28.34
1960 (wages)	£25.00	£474.40
1964 (wages)	£100.00	£3,412.00
1965 (wages)	3.7/6^d	£108.20
1965 (house)	£1,950.00	£30,980.00
1967 (holiday)	£50.00	£744.70
1969	5/-	£3.38
1969	£13.00	£175.60
1969 (house)	£5,000.00	£67,530.00
1970 (wages)	£48.00	£609.20
1970 (wages)	£84.00	£1,066.00
1971	£10.00	£116.00

Ref: www.measuringworth.com